THE JOY OF
FLYING

Other TAB books by the author:

Dedication:

To Lambert Brown, my instructor, mentor, and friend. Your guidance has inspired me to be pilot-in-command of much more than airplanes.

THE JOY OF
FLYING

by Robert J. Traister

MODERN AVIATION SERIES

TAB BOOKS Inc.

BLUE RIDGE SUMMIT, PA. 17214

FIRST EDITION

SECOND PRINTING

Printed in the United States of America

Reproduction or publication of the content in any manner, without express permission of the publisher, is prohibited. No liability is assumed with respect to the use of the information herein.

Copyright © 1981 by TAB BOOKS Inc.

Library of Congress Cataloging in Publication Data

Traister, Robert J.
    The joy of flying.

    Includes index.
    1. Private flying.   2. Airplanes, Private.
I. Title.
TL721.4.T7   629.132′5217   81-9199
ISBN 0-8306-2321-3 (pbk.)   AACR2

Contents

Preface

Since the dawn of man, earthbound residents have looked skyward with a yearning for the freedom that not too long ago was the sole realm of most birds and a select mammal or two. Man's obsession with flight began in very ancient times and for persons like Leonardo da Vinci, it encompassed a lifetime of design and experimentation. The first airborne "machines" were designed by ancient scientists who noted that smoke from a campfire ascended. A bag filled with this smoke would also be carried aloft. Centuries passed before these bags would reach a developmental stage where man could be carried along with them for short periods of time. Even today, the hot-air balloon is popular among enthusiasts.

The Wright Brothers are credited with the invention of the airplane, a device which is capable of sustained, powered flight. But many years before them, man was taking to the air in ancient equivalents of today's hang gliders.

In the 1980s, the teachings required to pilot an aircraft are, like the aircraft themselves, available to almost everyone who enjoys reasonably good health. In these modern times, men, women and children still look skyward with their imaginations, conjuring up feelings of what it must be like to fly. Unfortunately, many of these folks progress no further than this. Almost anyone who *truly* has a desire to become a private pilot can do so, even on a tight budget.

The learning experiences itself can be helpful in almost everything else the student will attempt in life. The practical aspects and advantages of holding a private pilot's license are equally balanced by the pure fun and enjoyment which can be experienced by this sport, hobby, or even occupation.

Today, flying is neither difficult nor dangerous, providing that proper instruction has been given and these teachings absorbed and continually practiced. Modern aircraft are equipped with safety features which far outweigh those of automobiles.

Flying is challenging. This pursuit does not require a special individual, only special procedures and aviation habits. It is interesting to note that in many states, a person may be a licensed pilot in command of a private aircraft before he or she is eligible, through age, to hold a driver's license.

Men, women, and teenagers make up the private pilot community in the United States and in many other countries. These are people like you, only they have taken practical steps to transform a dream into reality.

This book can be thought of as an introduction to private flying. Many aspects of aircraft, rules and regulations, and flying procedures are included, and they are balanced out with discussions of the many pleasurable activities which licensed pilots enjoy regularly.

Flying is *not* for the select few. This may have been the case only a few decades ago, but today, more and more everyday people are entering the world of aviation. If you have the desire and drive necessary, you too can join this community, forever casting off your earthly ties.

Robert J. Traister

Chapter 1

Everyday People
and Private Airplanes

Almost everyone has expressed an urge at one time or another to learn to fly an airplane. As children, each time a small plane flew overhead we would wonder what it must be like to have an eagle's view of the surroundings we see only from the ground. Our imaginings may have taken us into the cockpit which we thought surely must house a wealth of meters, controls, and highly complex instrumentation. Many people still think of flying as adventuresome and even dangerous. This, coupled with the idea of traveling in a different realm, has served to keep flying in the top ten of things we hope to do *someday*.

For many people, a flight on a commercial jet is the only above-ground traveling experience that has ever been encountered. This is a rather remote way of becoming initiated to flying, as a jet passenger rarely, if ever, gets to see the cockpit which is the control center for the entire trip. The cockpit has many extensions through radio links with control towers and a multitude of ground base services. All the jet airline passenger really experiences is what it's like to be airborne—not what it's like to really *fly*.

Some readers may have already been prompted to pay a visit to a local airport facility to watch small planes take off and land, taxi to and from the runway, and a few may even have sat inside the cockpit of a small, private plane. Space, or the lack of it, is probably one of the first true factors of small aircraft design which comes as a surprise. Most single engine private airplanes have rather small cockpits. Even the larger single-engine planes provide less passenger space than a standard Volkswagon automobile. Figure 1-1 shows the interior of light aircraft which is designed to hold four persons. The instrument panel would appear to be highly complex, but this complexity is quickly removed upon learning the purpose of the various instruments. Those readers who can remember back to their first time behind the wheel of an automobile can bear some similarities between this experience and sitting behind the yoke of their first airplane.

One of the biggest misconceptions about flying airplanes is that it is a very difficult thing to do. This is absolutely untrue. It is anomalous to note that many pilots obtain their licenses to fly private airplanes *before* they are eligible to even try for their driver's licenses. This is due principally to age. A person may receive a pilot's license at age 16, whereas in some states a bona fide driver's license cannot be issured at this tender age. The next time a plane flies over you, you might consider the possibility that it is being properly flown by an individual, male or female, who is still considered to be a child from a legal standpoint. Indeed, a surprisingly large number of people have been licensed on their sixteenth birthdays, having taken flying lessons up to the time when they could legally be licensed. Like most every other pursuit, starting young has certain major advantages as preconceived fears and prejudices are not as numerous as in a more experienced adult. Simply stated, a flight instructor needs to reverse fewer tendencies in a young student to pave the way for good piloting habits than would be the case if he were training a 35-year old adult.

Lest this discussion lead the reader to believe that it's simpler to hop into an airplane and fly to a specific destination than to make the same trip in an automobile, it should be pointed out that the rules and methods of flying are completely different than for land travel in an automobile. Undoubtedly, if many of the absolute musts of safe flying were brought into automobile travel, there would be far fewer automotive accidents on our nations's highways.

In the first place, you *never* just hop into an airplane, start the engine and take off. This is a sure formula for a mishap. The first lesson learned by a student pilot is the *ground check*. Before the engine is ever started, the pilot performs his walk-around inspection. This will usually start at the engine cowl and will continue in a counter-clockwise configuration all around the entire aircraft. The cowl flap is lifted in order to check the oil level, bleed the gas lines, check all hoses and perform a fairly thorough visual inspection of the powerplant. The air intakes are checked for blockages. This is important, as birds, insects, and small rodents will sometimes build nests in these cavities. If not discovered and corrected, these occurrences could cause engine failure in flight. After the powerplant has been operationally okayed, the pilot will check the propeller for any significant nicks in the blade. These can occur from small stones striking this device upon takeoff or landing. Small nicks are unavoidable and quite common, but any signs of significant damage are reason enough to delay the flight until repairs can be effected. The walk-around inspection continues with the pilot checking the tire inflation and general condition. The wing surfaces are checked by hand, again looking for signs of surface deterioration and distortion. The ailerons, which are control surfaces on the wings, are thoroughly checked for signs of damage or possible blockage. The pilot will then proceed to the tail of the aircraft, checking surfaces here for similar signs of deterioration. The rudder is examined closely, along with the tailwheel if the aircraft under examination has one. A portion of fuel is then drained from the aircraft into a clear glass bottle, and the pilot looks for signs of bubbles which indicate the presence of water infiltration. If bubbles are noted, more fuel is drained until they disappear. Water will usually collect at the lowest point in the fuel tank or tanks, as it is heavier than gasoline. Water contamination can cause an aircraft engine to fail completely in flight or to operate at less than peak horsepower.

Many other checks may be made in the walk-around inspection. The points discussed here are mere highlights of all that must be done. When the pilot finally enters the cockpit, a check is made

Fig. 1-1. Interior view of a light aircraft designed for four persons.

of battery power, gauge operation (for those gauges which operate from electrical power), fuel level, and other criteria. After priming the engine, the pilot will check to make certain the propeller is *clear*. This means that no object, animal, or person is anywhere near the unmoving propeller. He or she will then open the window vents or doors of the aircraft and literally yell, "CLEAR!" as loudly as possible. This lets everyone and everything know that the engine is about to be started. Once the engine is activated, some immediate gauge checks are mandatory to make certain that oil pressure and other vital engine operating parameters are within preset minimums and maximums.

At this point, the pilot will begin to taxi toward the runway, stopping just short of this goal in order to check for aircraft approaching from any direction. The pilot will usually radio that he is taxiing onto the runway to let any unseen aircraft know of his intentions. Before actually taking off, a thorough inspection is made of all controls by working the rudder pedals and the aileron yoke and visually examining their effect on the control surfaces. If everything passes so far, the engine is brought up to a high rpm with the wheel brakes locked. The ignition system is checked. In an aircraft, this consists of two magnetos, two spark plugs for each cylinder, ignition leads, and a magneto switch. Oil pressure is again checked and the pilot listens for any sounds of rough engine operation. Other parameters which will learn about later are also thoroughly checked.

If all of the checks indicate a perfectly functioning flight system, the plane will then be lined up on the runway and the takeoff begun. The entire process discussed in basic will be repeated for each and every takeoff. To deviate from this procedure would be dangerous and illegal, as the rules and regulations governing the operation of aircraft *require* that the pilot ascertain the correct functioning of his plane before taking off.

Getting back to earth again (figuratively speaking), let's compare this portion of flying with driving an automobile. When you drive to your job, you usually simply get in the automobile, start the engine, possibly adjust the seat and rearview mirror, and then pull off. A great many traffic accidents occur due to faulty automotive equipment. How many of these defects might be discovered before your vehicle was ever in motion if a walk-around inspection were performed before every trip? Knowing this, it may be an easy job to discover a neighborhood pilot. He or she is probably the person who walks completely around the automobile, possibly with a tire pressure gauge, checking for over or under-inflation and for the general condition of the tires. This same person will often lift the hood briefly just to see if any "varmints" have taken up residency within the engine compartment. Those of you who have had the experience of disentangling a cat, squirrel or other small animal from the fan belt of your family automobile may appreciate what an under-the-hood check can accomplish. When the engine is started, you may even hear it being revved gently to allow the driver to check its general performance. The windshield wipers, signal lights, parking and driving lights, along with the horn, may even be activated just to make sure everything is working in a normal manner.

Now, you may be thinking that this is a ridiculous waste of time and energy, but is it really? If everything is operational, the entire process usually takes less than three minutes. And if everything is not operational, isn't it worth these three minutes to find out about it? It is a fact that all safe pilots respect all means of transportation and are highly safety-conscious. It is for this reason that statistics will prove that the most dangerous part of flying may be the trip from home to the airport in your automobile.

FLYING FOR EVERYONE

Flying is not a pursuit only of the rich. It is a means of transportation, a hobby, a sport, and even an occupation for almost anyone who would like to get involved. Figure 1-2 shows a typical single-engine aircraft which retails for about $35,000.00. It is a four-seat aircraft and is very popular with a large number of flying enthusiasts. Admittedly, this is quite a price to pay by one person who generally wants to pursue the hobby aspect of flying, but used models are available at much lower prices. Or several pilots may wish to form a partnership, splitting the cost between all of the owners. There are many other ways to go about buying an airplane and these will be discussed later.

The largest number of weekend pilots will elect to rent an airplane by the hour rather than to buy. Almost all local airports offer flying schools and airplane rentals for reasonable prices. There are "wet" and "dry" rentals. The former refers to airplane rentals with fuel. The latter is without fuel and costs a bit less. Aircraft are equipped with engine use time indicators or "clocks" which begin running the moment the engine is started. Average rental with fuel for the Cessna Skyhawk runs about thirty-five to forty dollars per hour on a one-time basis. Smaller and larger

Fig. 1-2. Single-engine aircraft which retails for about $35,000.

aircraft will be proportionally higher and lower in cost. This assumes relatively new aircraft are being rented. This, too, sounds like a lot; but if you are carrying yourself and three other persons, it breaks down to less than $10.00 per person per hour. If you only want to fly solo, a two-passenger airplane might be chosen and would probably cost considerably less.

There are many many different types of used aircraft on the market and due to the care and maintenance, along with maintenance logs that are required of all aircraft, planes thirty or more years old can be obtained and flown in complete safety. Some of these planes can be purchased for less than $5,000 and will provide many years of useful service to the owners or owner. A complete discussion of aircraft ownership will be presented in another chapter.

What can you do with an airplane and a pilot's license? You can productively while away an afternoon improving your technique, seeing the sights, and thoroughly enjoying the quiet remoteness which many people find in flying. This pursuit would compare with a Sunday drive in your automobile. If you like to travel, many otherwise unreachable points of interest can be on your itinerary within an hour's traveling time. A leisurely trip of 110 miles to a location and back in the same day may not be so leisurely if accomplished with an automobile. A minimum of five hours travel time would have to be alloted; but using most typical light airplanes, this time an be cut by about three hours, depending upon wind conditions.

If you're a businessman who must travel to many different locations, an airplane might be able to *save* you money. From a practical standpoint, Americans spend billions of dollars every year in entertainment pursuits. These include swimming, camping, skiing, and a multitude of others. Flying can be a relaxation in itself and can even enable you to take advantage of other leisure time activities.

Certain portions of the country offer events especially for pilots which are called "Fly-Ins." These are usually a part of more traditional events. For example, in the author's home town of Front Royal, Virginia, a local attraction, Skyline Caverns, features a "Caverns Fly-In." Pilots from all over the East Coast are invited to fly into the local airport and be chauffered by automobile for a day of activities and tours at the underground caverns. The airport especially gears up for the increased activity, as do motels in the area, in order to provide a community-wide offer of hospitality to visiting pilots and their families. In this manner, out-of-state visitors get the opportunity to have a weekend of fun with other persons who are also pilots. Old friendships are renewed, new ones made, and flying is the talk of the day.

Many resort areas are opening and operating their own airport facilities. Even the smaller, less traveled locales are getting on the bandwagon. Bryce Resort in Virginia offers golf, skiing, tennis, horseback riding, sailing and all of the usual resort activities, along with a small but professionally run and maintained airport. Many who own homes and property on the resort grounds work in metropolitan areas and fly back on weekends to take advantage of the country living. Without air access, these activities would be impossible for many. As an additional bonus, many pilots in neighboring towns and cities may fly into Bryce Resort for an evening of dining and music, returning at the end of the evening to their hometowns, many of which lie within a half hour's flight of the resort. Due to winding mountain roads, this same trip by automobile might take several hours.

This text is aimed at the individual who is interested in pursuing a private pilot's license. This is a grade of license which most pilots obtain for personal flying. Some go on to obtain a commercial pilot's license which allows them to charge for transporting materials and passengers to different points. This aspect of flying will not heavily discussed in this book which will concentrate mainly on personal use. A private pilot's license only allows the licensee to fly for pleasure and personal business. It does not entitle the holder to charge fees in order to make a profit through his or her flying abilities. This does not mean that passengers cannot help to pay for the pilot's expenses. This can be compared to a group of friends taking an automobile trip with everybody absorbing a portion of the gas costs.

With the price of gas today, fuel economy is an ever-present consideration. This also concerns the private pilot. Using the 1981 Cessna Skyhawk as an example, a pilot may be able to get in excess of 16 statute miles per gallon of gas. This will depend upon wind conditions, speed, and engine power setting. This may not sound like great gas mileage by automobile standards, but when you consider that air travel is line-of-sight, the mpg figure becomes a little more impressive. A road trip of forty miles could easily be thirty miles or less by air. Taking this into consideration, the airplane would easily equal in excess of 20 miles per gallon, comparing the two trips. With favorable wind conditions, the mpg figure could be significantly increased. Add to this the fact that you would be on the road for nearly an hour and in the plane for fifteen to twenty minutes, and the advantages of flying to a destination become very attractive.

Don't think that you can completely do away with your automobile, however, as flying has many limitations. Of course, if there is no airport at your destination, the trip is completely out of the question. Also, weather conditions will figure heavily in every trip you take as a future pilot. Gusting winds, rain, snow, sleet, fog and all the rest must be taken into consideration. It is not enough to know weather conditions just before takeoff. You must also know what they will be throughout the entire journey. Fortunately, excellent forecasting facilities are available to the pilot by radio or by telephone. These forecasting services will be discussed in detail in a later portion of the book. Many trips which are made in complete safety in automobiles would be unthinkable by the average private pilot in an airplane due to weather conditions.

The author likes to compare travel by airplane and travel by automobile to cooking by microwave versus cooking with a standard oven. The microwave oven offers a lot of conveniences over the latter. It cooks more quickly, and thus conserves energy. On the other hand, some foods just don't taste right when cooked in a microwave oven and, of necessity, must go the route of the old electric range. It is generally more efficient to cook in the microwave, but it's not always possible to do so and still obtain pleasing results. The same can be said of flying, which is a quicker means of transportation,, but certain circumstances require automotive travel for pleasing and safe results. Just as the microwave oven will probably never replace the electric range, the airplane will never replace ground transportation. The two work hand in hand, each enabling the other to function more efficiently.

Family outings are probably some of the most rewarding for the average private pilot. Indeed, in many families, the husband, wife and even the older children may all be pilots. Young children readily adapt to flying and may even become immune to the thrills of the experience after only a few flights. Whole families can cover great distances in complete comfort and safety and cross-country flights are certainly not unheard of. Flying vacations may be planned in the winter months and begun when the children are on summer break. Alternately, many Eastern families may opt for a winter vacation during Christmas break. The *ne plus ultra* may be a trip to the Bahamas. This is accomplished in several legs, the first being a flight from the home state to Southern Florida. From here, it is less than an hour to the nearest of the Bahamian Islands. This island group boasts quite a number of airports, as aircraft make up one of the major forms of inter-island transportation. After the first landing, the family may decide to base their operations from a central island, flying to others in the chain on different days. This is called "island hopping" and the generally excellent Bahamian weather is most conducive to these activities. As an added thrill, everyone gets to fly through the Bermuda Triangle, both coming and going. Unlike the many books and television specials on this subject would have you believe, the safety record for private aircraft along this route is very high. This is probably due to the excellent visibility and lack of heavy air traffic.

This discussion has covered only a few of the many possibilities and pursuits that an average individual, such as yourself, might find in flying. You certainly do not have to be a superman to take up this activity. You should be in generally good health, although very few medical conditions completely limit persons from obtaining their licenses. "But don't I have to have 20/20 vision?" you might ask. The answer is *no*. Many private pilots are nearsighted or farsighted (just like every other segment of the population), but their vision deficiencies have been offset by corrective lenses.

SUMMARY

Regardless of who you are and what your past experiences may be, you can probably qualify to become a private pilot. Student pilot's licenses may be issued at age 16, while a private pilot's license is available to individuals 17 years of age and over. Technically there is no maximum age limit, although all applicants must be able to pass a physical examination for a Third Class Medical Certificate.

By checking with a nearby local airport, you can find out more about costs involved in trying for your license. Most facilities offer programs which include ground schooling, dual and solo flight instruction, and all necessary books in a package price which is most reasonable and can often be paid for on a monthly basis. You may even be able to join a flying club which allows members to take lessons in the jointly owned airplane or airplanes.

Flying is fun, rewarding, and challenging for a vast cross section of the population. It is a pursuit which is enjoyed by both young and old, male and female, white collar and blue collar workers. No one group or category seems to have any special advantages over another. Flying, then, would seem to make all men (and women) brothers (and sisters). Nothing about it is extremely complicated or hard to do; and chances are, there's a local airport within a short driving distance from your home where you could begin today if you have a mind to.

Chapter 2

Knowing The Airplane

Flight and flying devices have been with us for hundreds of years. Hot-air balloons were probably the first "flying machines" to take man aloft, although these first flights were always at the end of a tether. The balloon has survived even to modern times, where hot-air ballooning is an ever-growing sport for enthusiasts from coast to coast. In recent years, a hot-air balloon was piloted non-stop across the Atlantic Ocean.

Gliders were probably the next step in the evolution to the modern airplane. Hundreds of years ago, these were very flimsy devices which more closely resembled the hang gliders of today. True gliders are very popular in modern times, and glider clubs now exist at many local airports. Today, the traditional glider is more often referred to as a sailplane. This type of craft has extremely good aerodynamic characteristics and allows the pilot to test his skill in controlling the craft to take advantage of air currents in order to achieve high altitudes for extended periods of time.

Today, the most commonly used type of aircraft is the airplane. They come in all sizes, shapes and colors and are designed for a multitude of services and applications. Airplanes have many different types of classifications which are derived from their intended uses, types of landing gear, wing configurations, number of engines, and other factors.

TYPES OF AIRPLANE

Figure 2-1 shows a single-engine airplane with *fixed* landing gear. This is one category of airplane which has a single powerplant

Fig. 2-1. Single-engine airplane with fixed landing gear (courtesy Piper Aircraft Corp.).

and propeller and landing gear which is always fixed in place. It is unmovable. Much variation can be found in this classification of airplane. Designs range from single-seat craft with 50 horsepower engines to planes which seat seven persons and have over 300 horsepower. Obviously, the planes just described are very different; and yet, they both would fall into the same basic classification.

Figure 2-2 shows another airplane which has *retractable* landing gear. It is very similar to the previous model shown, but its performance characteristics in flight are far better due to the fact that the landing gear can be withdrawn into the body of the airplane. This is shown in Fig. 2-3. When the landing gear is withdrawn or *retracted*, the aerodynamic structure becomes much more efficient and wind drag is decreased. Therefore, the plane with retractable gear will usually boast higher speeds and/or better fuel economy than one with fixed gear.

All of the planes pictured so far have had what is known as *tricycle* landing gear. This means that a nosewheel is used beneath the engine cowling, along with the main gear which protrudes from beneath the cabin or from below the wings, depending upon airplane design. Figure 2-4 shows a plane with *conventional* landing gear. This arrangement uses a tailwheel along with the main gear. The term conventional is a holdover from the days when tailwheel aircraft were the rule rather than the exception. When the nosewheel was introduced, this new landing gear setup was different from what has been used before; hence, the term conventional to describe the old system. It can be correctly stated

Fig. 2-2. A retractable gear airplane with gear extended. Notice the door which covers the right wheel. This encloses the wheel when it is retracted, making the plane aerodynamically smooth (courtesy Beech Aircraft Corp.).

today that the majority of modern airplanes are equipped with tricycle gear. Conventional gear is rather *un*conventional in these modern times, with the exception of utility aircraft which are designed for dirt fields and other unpaved areas. Conventional gear aircraft are also affectionately referred to as *taildraggers*.

Two standard wing configurations are used for most modern single-engine aircraft. The plane in Fig. 2-4 is a high wing model with the wing located above the cockpit. Figure 2-5 shows a low wing plane. The difference is immediately apparent and arguments

Fig. 2-3. The same airplane shown in the previous photograph but with gear retracted. This is the standard flight configuration for such a plane (courtesy Beech Aircraft Corp.).

Fig. 2-4. An airplane with conventional landing gear. Notice that the main gear is moved forward of the cockpit and a tailwheel is located behind (courtesy Cessna Aircraft Co.).

persist to this day over which is the superior design. Each has its own advantages and disadvantages. For aerial photography work, the high wing design offers the advantage of not obstructing as much of the view below as would be the case in a low wing plane. On the other hand, the low wing design provides better lateral visibility for the pilot. This enables him to better see approaching planes from the left, right and above. Most aircraft companies concentrate on one design or the other. The high wing planes pictured so far have all been manufactured by Cessna Aircraft Company in Wichita, Kansas, which, to many people, is the leader in the manufacture of high wing aircraft. All of their single-engine designs use the high wing configuration, with the exception of

Fig. 2-5. An example of a light aircraft using low wing design (courtesy Piper Aircraft Corp.).

three models which are low wing single-seaters designed for crop dusting purposes. Cessna's twin-engine airplane are of the traditional low wing design, with the exception of one model (the Skymaster) which uses the high wing with centerline thrust engines, one at the front and the other at the rear of the cabin.

Going in the other direction, Piper Aircraft Corporation, Beech Aircraft Corporation and Mooney Aircraft Corporation have pretty much converted to all low wing design. Piper still offers the old standard "Piper Cub", although today it's known as the Super Cub. It is of traditional high wing design and still looks very similar to the Cubs of forty years ago.

It is easy to understand why manufacturers tend to stay with one basic type of airplane design. The millions upon millions of dollars spent on research and development of airplanes usually preclude simultaneous development of two radically different designs. It can be safely said that the recognized manufacturers of high wing craft offer the public the best available in this design configuration, while the recognized manufacturers of low wing planes offer the same in another design. It is up to the plane buyer to decide which configuration best suits his or her operational needs.

Figure 2-6 shows a twin-engine aircraft which is another plane classification. In order to be certified to pilot this classification of craft, the pilot must obtain a twin-engine rating for his private pilot's license which, by itself, permits the pilot to fly only single-engine airplanes.

Fig. 2-6. A twin-engine aircraft requires a pilot to have a special certification to a private pilot's license in order to act as pilot in command (courtesy Piper Aircraft Corp.).

PARTS OF THE AIRPLANE

Airplane wings are extremely strong even though they are designed to be very lightweight. The true strength of the wing is found in the *spars* which run the entire length of the wing from tip to root and bear the major part of the bending wingload. The wing sections will flex up and down due to air turbulence and different loading factors. The spars are able to absorb much of this pressure. G-forces can also cause the wing to twist. *Ribs* maintain the shape by running perpendicularly to the spars from the leading edge to each wing section. The metal or cloth skin which covers the elements also absorbs much of the load. Figure 2-7 shows a cross section of a typical aircraft wing. To prevent wing buckling, additional components known as *stringers* are found running parallel with the wing spars. These place a certain tension between the root and tip, causing the entire wing to be more stable.

Almost all aircraft use hollow cavities in the wing sections to mount the fuel tanks. This applies to high and low wing designs alike, although some planes offer auxiliary storage by means of a small tank within the main body section. High wing planes can take full advantage of gravity feed of fuel to the engine. Low wing planes cannot use this type of feed, as the tanks will normally be located below the engine fuel intake. These planes use engine-driven fuel pumps, along with electric pumps or boosters for initial starting and critical flight procedures. The electric pump assures that adequate fuel will be fed to the engine should the motor-driven pump fail to operate. Both systems are used for takeoffs and landing, with the electric pump being shut down in normal flight. Some high wing planes, especially those using fuel injection, may also offer electric booster pumps.

Figure 2-8 shows the location of the *flaps* and *ailerons* which are hinged to the trailing edge of the airplane wing. The ailerons are located closer to the wing tips, while the flaps are mounted between the body and the ailerons. The ailerons move in reverse order; that is, when the left aileron is in an up position, the right one is pointing downward. These devices make the aircraft roll or bank and are controlled by the left or right turning of the aircraft yoke or wheel. The flaps move in the same direction, which is always downward, from their resting position on the aircraft wing. Flap extension may be controlled by an electric motor or by mechanical linkage to a hand control. They are primarily used during the takeoff and landing phases of a flight in order to produce more lift or to establish a glidepath. Flap extension is determined in degrees. Mechanical linkage systems have controls with indentations at various degree settings from 10 to about 40 degrees. Electrical systems continuously indicate flap extension on a mechanical meter. Some aircraft, especially the older types, may not have flaps. They are not absolutely necessary but do allow for flexibility in landing speed and can also assist in takeoff from short landing fields.

The body, or *fuselage*, of the airplane is the core of the structure. Everything attaches to this section. This includes the wing, tail assembly, landing gear (in low wing planes, the main gear is often attached to the wing sections), and engine. The length of the fuselage usually determines the number of passengers the plane is designed to transport.

There are two basic types of fuselage construction. Most modern planes use a *semi-monocoque* method that allows the aluminum alloy skin to carry a major portion of physical stress associated with flight. Stringers such as the type used in wing construction, along with circular formers, provide a network for the alloy sheet to conform with.

Another construction method which is more traditionally found in older planes uses a framework of steel tubing over which a fabric is stretched. This is called *truss-type* construction and physical stresses are absorbed by this framework.

The tail section of an airplane is called the *empennage*. Shown in Fig. 2-9, this portion of the airplane includes a *vertical fin* or *stabilizer*, a *rudder*, the *horizontal stabilizer* and a movable *elevator*. In some planes, the horizontal stabilizer is movable in an up/down motion, thus doing away with the need for a separate, hinged elevator section. The movable horizontal stabilizer or elevator is

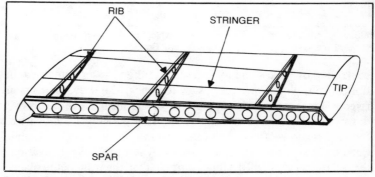

Fig. 2-7. Cross-sectional view of a typical aircraft wing.

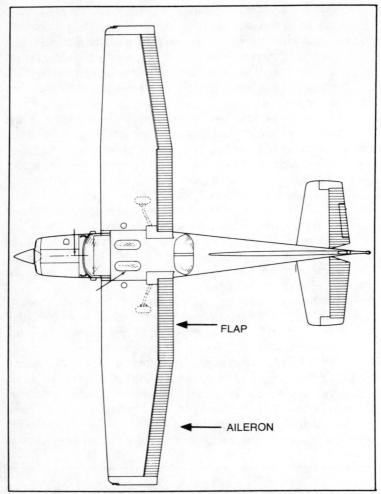

FLAP

AILERON

Fig. 2-8. Location of the flaps and ailerons which are hinged to the trailing edge of the airplane wing (courtesy Cessna Aircraft Co.).

controlled by a back and forth motion of the yoke or wheel within the cockpit. When the yoke is pulled back, the elevator section rises. This causes the rear section of the airplane to be forced downward due to air resistance. The front portion of the plane is then higher in relation to the tail and the plane begins to climb. Pushing the yoke forward moves the elevator to the down position, the tail rises to a slightly higher altitude than the front of the plane, and the craft descends.

The rudder is controlled by two pedals on the floor of the cockpit, which are worked by the pilot's feet. These pedals also control the nose or tail wheel, which steers the plane when on the ground. In the air, pressing in on the left rudder pedal moves the rudder to the left. Wind resistance against the rudder pushes the tail toward the right, moving the front of the plane toward the left. The opposite occurs when the right rudder is depressed.

On the ground, the plane is steered only by foot control of the pilot. The wheel or yoke has no control on the ground maneuvers and is only used after the plane is airborne. Occasionally, some

Fig. 2-9. The tail section or empennage, includes a vertical fin, rudder, stabilizer, and a moveable elevator.

craft are designed with the rudder tied into the aileron yoke controls. In these designs, the plane is then steered on the ground and controlled in the air only by the yoke.

The engine, or powerplant, of an airplane is attached to the firewall of the fuselage by means of an engine mount. An engine *cowling* is used to enclose the powerplant and serves many purposes. By shrouding the engine, it is able to duct cooling air around the cylinders. It also provides streamlining to reduce drag by efficiently passing air over the nose of the plane. Figure 2-10 shows the attachment of these parts to the fuselage of the plane.

The airplane propeller may be attached directly to the crankshaft of the aircraft engine or it may be gear driven. It is actually a small wing or airfoil. As shown in Fig. 2-11, the propeller blades are twisted to allow them to effectively bite into the air at the proper angles to produce forward lift. The propeller is often referred to as a revolving wing, the principle by which helicopters operate.

INSTRUMENTATION

Figure 2-12 shows the instrument and control panel of a large single-engine aircraft. The pilot in command would normally be seated behind the left yoke (wheel) where most of the flight instruments are positioned in the panel. Directly over the center of the yoke is the *rate-of-climb indicator*. To its left is the *directional gyro* which indicates the course setting. The first instrument indicates the air speed at which the plane is ascending or descending. The indicator is currently pointing to zero, meaning that the plane is doing neither. Naturally, the plane containing this instrument panel is parked, but in normal flight, the pilot attempts to keep his aircraft in this position until he desires to climb or descend.

Directly above the rate-of-climb indicator is the *altimeter*, which indicates altitude above sea level. This does *not* indicate the plane's actual altitude above the earth. The indicator needle indicates approximately 3,350 feet as the altitude, which would mean that the plane was tied down at an airport whose elevation was this distance above sea level. The altimeter is most important in almost every aspect of flying. FAA rules and regulations require pilots who fly above certain altitudes to maintain specific altitudes depending upon their course heading. For instance, a pilot flying in one direction might be required to keep his craft at even altitudes such as 4,000, 6,000, or 8,000 feet above sea level. A plane traveling in the opposite direction would be required to fly at odd altitude increments of 3,000, 5,000, and 7,000 feet. Aviation weather forecasters provide reports of wind conditions at various altitudes, so a pilot wishing to take advantage of optimum wind conditions for his planned course would decide from the forecast where he or she could obtain a tail wind or least head wind conditions. The plane would then be flown to the best altitude by using the altimeter as an indicator.

To the left of the altimeter is the *gyro horizon*, which indicates the position of the wings in relationship to an artificial horizon. A pilot will use this instrument to bank the plane to the desired angle to effect a maneuver. To the left of this instrument is the *airspeed indicator*. This is equivalent to the speedometer in the automobile. However, airspeed indicators are aptly named, as they measure the speed of air, not the speed of the plane. In perfectly still air, an airspeed indicator reading of 120 knots would mean that the plane was traveling at the same 120 knot speed in relation to the ground. But if the plane were flying into a 20 knot headwind, this would mean that the plane's ground speed would be only 100 knots. With a theoretical 120 knot headwind, the plane would be unmoving in relation to the ground (zero ground speed), but the airspeed indicator would still read 120 knots. For practical purposes, it can be said that the airspeed indicator reads the velocity of the air which crosses the airplane's wings. The converse is also true. If the plane were flying with a 10 knot tailwind, then an airspeed indication of 120 knots would mean a ground speed of 130 knots.

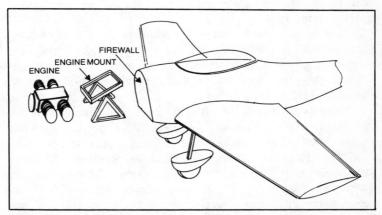

Fig. 2-10. Attachment of engine and associated powerplant parts to the airframe.

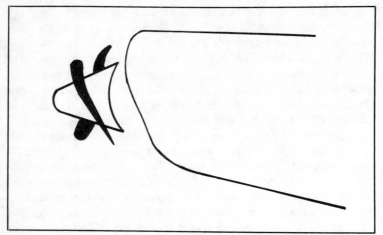

Fig. 2-11. Propeller blades are twisted to allow them to effectively bite into the air.

Below the airspeed indicator is the *turn coordinator*, which allows the pilot to judge how much rudder pedal to use in a turn to cause the tail of the plane to properly follow the wings. If proper coordination is not achieved, the plane will slip sideways rather than turning as desired.

Radio navigation equipment is located between the two yokes, while the *trim controls* which keep the plane level in flight are located below them at the bottom of the panel. Most planes have dual controls and can be flown from either the left or right seat. However, most of the crucial flight instruments are located on the left side of the panel.

Engine instrumentation is found in front or the right-hand yoke. At the top are fuel gauges and in the second grouping, oil temperature, pressure and cylinder head temperature gauges are found. In this plane, an auxiliary altimeter is also located on the far right of the instrument panel.

Directly in front of the left grip on the right-hand yoke is the *tachometer*, which indicates engine rpm. This is used to bring the engine speed to the correct setting for various cruise and climbing conditions. Below this control is the *flap lever*, which extends these attachments to the wing sections to the degree desired. Another instrument, the *clock*, which indicates the total number of hours on the airplane engine, is located in the bottom portion of the tachometer's face. This is activated whenever the engine is in operation.

There are many other controls on this well-outfitted panel, but the ones discussed are those which are most often encountered in light aircraft. Again, this panel is very well bedecked with instrumentation. Many planes will not be so ideally equipped. To the newcomer, the prospect of all of these instruments and controls may be quite frightening, but it must be remembered that this equipment greatly aids and simplifies the pilot's job. After a few hours of instruction, the various dials and knobs, their uses and meanings will become second nature and will be continually observed by the pilot as part of the routine of flying.

Figure 2-13 shows a more complex cockpit view of the controls found in the twin-engine Beechcraft Duke B60. This panel would seem to be far more complex than the one previously discussed, but many instruments have been duplicated for both the left and right seat positions. The console at the center bottom of this picture contains the throttle controls and associated electronics and linkages for the two engines. At the center right of the instrument panel is a weather radar device which is often found in better outfitted aircraft. With this instrument, weather conditions for miles around can be partially interpreted. Notice the dual rudder controls at the bottom left and right of this picture. A flight time indicator is also included. This is found at the center of the left seat yoke.

Instrumentation can be a very significant part of the purchase price of an aircraft. Up to a point, the more instrumentation you have, the more efficiently you can fly your plane. Think back to your first few lessons behind the wheel of an automobile. The

Fig. 2-12. Well-equipped instrument panel of a single-engine airplane (courtesy Cessna Aircraft Co.).

31

Fig. 2-13. Front cockpit view of the instrument panel and controls in a twin engine aircraft (courtesy Beech Aircraft Corp.).

instrumentation here seemed to be highly complex and mysterious for a while, but after a few hours of instruction, these instruments became familiar and enabled you to drive more efficiently. Generally speaking, aircraft instrumentation is no more difficult to learn than that found in an automobile. It is simply different. Learning the instrumentation comes easily to almost all student pilots who will depend upon it during all flights to provide constant input for safe and efficient piloting.

SUMMARY

This chapter has touched lightly on the various aspects of control surfaces, general construction, and instrumentation of airplanes. The science behind their reasons for functioning is highly complex, but the operation and control of these items has been designed with the human being in mind. They are all made to be an extension of the pilot's movement and senses. They can be thought of along with yourself as pilot, as a two-way radio system. You and the instruments and controls all have the ability to transmit and receive. When the instruments transmit a specific condition to you, you receive this data and respond by transmitting correct data back into the system. You become a part of the controls and instrumentation, just as they become a part of you. It is this coordination and coupling between pilot and aircraft, both melding into one, which enables us to travel safely by air.

Chapter 3

Getting Your License

Just like most other means of transportation, it is necessary to obtain a license in order to act as a pilot in an airplane. The progressions that are made in aircraft licenses are very similar to the steps taken in obtaining driver's permits. Just as many of us began driving automobiles while holding student operator's licenses, the beginning pilot also obtains what is commonly known as a student pilot's license. This is a misnomer of sorts, because this is really a Third Class Medical Certificate which is obtained from an FAA certified medical examiner. This, in itself, is considered to be the student pilot license when an instructor signs the back indicating the student is qualified for solo flight.

From student pilot, the next logical step is to private pilot. From this point, the pilot may add special ratings, pursue a commercial pilot's license, or even go for the top of the line ATP or Air Transport Pilot's license. Each of these license grades entitles the holder to certain flying privileges.

SO YOU WANT TO FLY?

Now that you know a bit about the structuring of a pilot's license, let's start at the beginning and assume that you've never been in an airplane before but would like to get your license. The first step is to go to your local airport and sign up for flying lessons. It is necessary to delve a bit deeper into the term flying lessons, as this can mean a multitude of different things. In learning to fly, there is a lot more to it than simply knowing how to control the airplane. You must also know how to plot a course, react to other air traffic, correctly enter a flight pattern, and even be familiar with proper radio technique. Actual control of the airplane is only part of the overall art of proper flying.

Flying lessons can be broken down into two general categories: flight training and ground school. The former involves the actual time spent in the plane, while ground school identifies the vast amount of paperwork and book study required. Many local airports offer ground school at a reasonable fee for those interested in flying. Some ground schools may even be given at no charge. This is a smart business move for many airports, because once a person learns a little about the rules and regulations governing flying, they are almost certain to want to take flying lessons in the air. This is where the airport is able to recoup any financial losses from the ground school program.

Perhaps the author's experience in beginning his flying program might be of benefit to the reader, as it closely parallels the experiences of other pilots. It happened shortly before my eighteenth birthday and began with seeing a picture in a magazine of an elderly couple who had won a small, single-engine airplane in an industry contest. Up to this point, I had never considered flying in any way. Something seemed to click in my head and I wondered if I might be able to take flying lessons. Though living in a small town, I was able to find a listing for flight instruction in the yellow pages of the local phone directory. The airport facility offering these lessons was located in a town about twenty miles distant. An immediate phone call to the airport FBO (fixed-base operator) gave me no more details than "Come on over and we'll take you for a ride this afternoon." An hour later I was at the airport climbing into my first airplane. Unbelievable to me at the time, I was allowed to sit in the left seat (the pilot's seat) and was given the opportunity to actually fly the Piper Cherokee 150C after it was airborne and clear of the traffic pattern.

I was hooked. It didn't seem that hard to do, although I had no idea at the time of the broad range of responsibility a pilot has. The charge for the flight? Nothing! I was told by the instructor that if I wanted to continue I was to come back tomorrow with money in hand. This was in the late sixties and the going rate was $18.00 per hour for dual instruction. This broke down to about $14.00 per hour for the plane and $4.00 per hour for the instructor. Another $20.00 was spent at the onset for a log book, mechanical flight computer, and textbooks.

It was almost too easy, or so it seemed, for a small town boy to enter the exciting world of flying. The $18.00 per hour was quite a bit, but I was able to scrape up enough money to take two lessons per week. My instructor was very firm but fair and insisted upon strict adherence to every safety rule known to man. My confidence in him was immediately established and remains today.

INSTRUCTORS

It would be nice to say that I continued my flying lessons at an advanced pace and succeeded in getting my pilot's license a short time later. However, this did not come until over five years later. After I had had about four lessons, my instructor left the employ of this airport facility and I was suddenly presented with a new instructor whom I had never met before. He was obviously not as experienced (with people anyway) as my former instructor; and knowing that I had trained under the fellow he had replaced, I guess he was determined to show me how little I knew. I should say that this is not typical of a flight instructor. In any event, he succeeded in rattling me to the point where I could do practically nothing right. He took the controls himself and proceeded to fly this green student through the skies with the airplane in every imaginable configuration. This included dives and spins which I was really not prepared for. After about ten minutes of this nonsense, this green pilot was *truly* green from airsickness. I was chided for being a sissy and flown back to the airport, where I was told that I would need to un-learn some of the incorrect things my former instructor had taught me. At this point, I felt like I never wanted to fly again—and *didn't* for several years.

This was a highly unusual experience and is mentioned here only to point out to the reader that you should always know a bit about your flight instructor. Ninety-nine percent of them are the finest people you'll ever want to know; but as with all groups, there are some rotten ones out there as well. The villain mentioned in this story lasted another three weeks at the airport and was fired on the spot for disregarding flight rules. Since this time, I have had five or six different instructors, all of whom represent the ninety-nine percent. A bad egg among flight instructors is usually quickly detected and ousted from this elite group of men and women who are not only crack pilots but equally proficient in teaching their students.

During the initial period of training for a student pilot's license, the instructor will teach the basics of handling the aircraft.

This will include normal handling in level flight, climb to altitude, proper reading of the instruments, turns, etc. Additionally, emergency training will be practiced during almost every outing. This will include recovery from stalls, establishing a glide path, emergency landing areas, and many other techniques. After the actual flying lesson is ended, most instructors give students study assignments which involve learning rules and regulations, weather systems, radio navigation, loading, and dozens of other factors associated with flight.

A flight computer is shown in Fig. 3-1 and is used to perform a multitude of calculations involved in preparing for a flight. Some of the functions include plotting wind drift over a predetermined course, converting from statute to nautical miles and vice versa, trip time, and fuel consumption, to name just a few. This is an easy instrument to become acquainted with and quickly becomes indispensable to the student pilot.

Depending upon the student's progress, after approximately 15 hours of dual flight instruction, he or she may be "signed off." This means the instructor signs the medical certificate in the appropriate space, indicating the student has been certified by him to act as pilot-in-command of the specific aircraft type which was used for training. The medical certificate is obtainable by anyone in generally good health whose vision (corrected by lenses, if necessary) is at least 20/30 or better. It is given by an FAA certified medical examiner and merely indicates that the holder has no medical disorders which would impair his or her ability to act as pilot-in-command of an aircraft.

In order to be properly certified by your instructor for solo flight, you must complete three solo takeoffs and landings to a full stop. Once this has been accomplished, your license is signed and you may pilot the aircraft solo, but you may not carry any passengers. This means your flying from this point on will be done absolutely alone or with an instructor or other pilot holding a license rating of at least private pilot. Two student pilots may not fly together in the same aircraft without an instructor or private pilot present. Breaking this rule often means that the violator is grounded for an entire year and must start over again.

The purpose of the student pilot's license is to give the training pilot the opportunity to practice the procedures he or she has learned in the dual instruction phase of training. Being the sole pilot in charge of piloting an aircraft bears great responsibility and the student pilot assumes this responsibility during the first solo flight. There is no instructor in the cockpit to help out in a bad situation. The student must use learned abilities to prevent a bad situation from occurring in the first place.

THRILL OF THE SOLO

As is the case with most pilots, the author will never forget the mild April evening when he first soloed. The first five or six

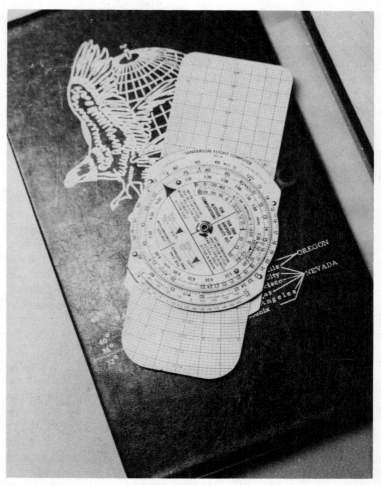

Fig. 3-1. A flight computer is an inexpensive device used to perform a multitude of calculations involved in flight navigation.

hours of dual flight training had gone by very easily, but the next five hours were fraught with difficulties and many frustrations. Then during the next two hours of flight time everything seemed to suddenly come together. Weather was excellent, and the Cessna 150 two-seater seemed to be an extension of my body. My instructor and I were doing practice landings, and after ten successful touchdowns in a row, he stepped out of the plane and said, "Do it by yourself."

It was nothing like I imagined it would be. I experienced not even a twinge of fear or doubt. This is a tribute more to the instructor than to myself. Immediately after I had departed the runway, climbing to pattern altitude, a light wind picked up. I made the proper corrections and thoroughly enjoyed the short flight around the pattern to effect an immediate landing on the same runway I had lifted off from a few minutes earlier. My first solo landing was as near perfect as is humanly possible. Even to this day, I have never made a better landing. After stopping the plane, I taxied back to the start of the runway, took off and landed again, then repeated the process once more for a total of three takeoffs and landings, as required.

My instructor contacted me by radio after the third landing and told me to go around once more and then bring the aircraft back to the hangar. The wind had picked up a bit more by this time but was blowing parallel to the runway, so there was no real problem. However, between the time I lifted off and the time I was approaching for a touchdown, a crosswind developed with some minor gusts. Just seconds before touchdown, a gust of wind caught the plane at just the right angle to effect what's known as a *balloon*. Just when you think you are about to touch down, the plane starts to climb. This is a common occurrence but was a bit unexpected at the time by myself and my instructor. As soon as I sensed the balloon, I immediately corrected by slowly pushing forward on the yoke. The plane settled onto the runway just as it was supposed to and exactly as my instructor and I had practiced so many times. He told me later that he was a bit concerned about the sudden wind, but I was already airborne before he discovered it. He also went on to say that I handled the situation in the proper manner. This served to build my confidence up even more. He then proceeded to chew me out for some ragged turns I had made during the solo flight and criticized a few other aspects of my flying that I felt I was proficient enough in to disregard. Looking back on this experience, I can see the psychology that was being used to prevent an exuberant neophyte from becoming too over-confident and possibly tackling something he was not yet qualified to handle.

Probably one of the most asked questions from persons interested in taking flying lessons is, "How many hours of flying time will be required before I can solo?" This is a valid question but is most difficult to answer. Some of the factors which will determine the answer include the student's ability to adapt to new environments, the number of times per week lessons are given, and prevailing weather conditions. This latter factor is surprising to quite a few people but plays a big part in student training. At certain times of the year and in specific locales, gusting winds may be a big problem. Most instructors prefer to allow their students to solo during the early morning or early evening hours when winds tend to be calm. A student who is certified for solo flight will often be restricted to flying only when crosswinds are below certain speeds until more flight proficiency is obtained.

Some people take to flying more readily than others. Many seem to have certain instinctive abilities toward operations in a flying environment, while others may require more time to adjust. Personality plays a great role here. Even-tempered students who go calmly about daily rituals often make better students, while excitable persons take longer to adjust to the differing conditions. This is not to say that students who are easily excited cannot or do not make good pilots; it just may take a few extra hours for this group to be properly trained. Certainly, very few of us can completely rid ourselves of some basic fears which are exploited during initial training sessions. Some of us react better to the control of these fears than others.

It is usually best to take lessons on a regular basis. If several weeks go by between lessons, some of the learned instincts may not be as sharp. The author's instructor started his student at the rate of about two lessons per week, building up to three after about five hours and then every day immediately before soloing. This allowed for gradual adjustment and an easier transition to the flying experience. After soloing, the student can then determine how often he or she would like to fly.

For most student pilots, between twelve and eighteen hours of dual instruction are normally required to be signed off for solo flight. Some earn their wings in slightly less instructional time, while others may require considerably more. There is no need to be in a rush, as all that you and your instructor should be concerned with is your ability to properly pilot an aircraft. It is much better to be signed off late than too early.

THE PRIVATE PILOT'S LICENSE

The private license is the one most student pilots are aiming for during the initial stages of their flight program. This is considered to be the general license of pilots and allows the holder to fly anywhere as long as weather conditions permit visual flight. Passengers may be transported by the holder of a private license but not on a "for pay" basis. There are ratings that may be obtained with your private license which certify you for flight in instrument conditions. This, of course, assumes that the airplane is properly and legally instrumented for these applications. As was previously mentioned, if you desire to fly twin-engine airplanes or helicopters, these ratings must also be obtained and require that additional flight instruction in these aircraft types be given by a certified instructor.

FAA rules and regulations place certain instructional requirements upon the person who wishes to qualify for the private license. Some of these include:

■ A total of at least 40 hours of dual flight instruction and solo flight time, which must include 20 hours of instruction from an authorized flight instructor. Of this 20 hours, there must be at least three hours of cross country time, three hours of night flying, including 10 takeoffs and landings at night, and three hours in airplanes in sole preparation for the private pilot flight test. This latter time must be within 60 days of the FAA flight test.

■ Twenty hours of solo flight time, including at least 10 hours in airplanes and 10 hours of cross country flight. Included in this 20 hours must be three solo takeoffs and landings to a full stop at an airport with an operating control tower.

Before you can be given an actual flight test by an FAA examiner, you must first pass a written examination. In order to take the written test, the applicant must:

■ Show that he or she has satisfactorily completed the ground instruction or home study course required by this part for the certificate or rating sought.

■ Present as personal identification an airman certificate, driver's license, or other official document.

■ Present a birth certificate or other official document showing that he or she meets the age requirement prescribed in this part for the certificate sought not later than two years from the date of application for the test.

Now, exactly what can you do with a private pilot's license? To start off with, you can load the entire family into an airplane and fly them all for a weekend outing or an exotic vacation. You can fly into controlled airports which do not allow pilots in command access unless he or she holds at least a license of this grade. Generally speaking, you may use the airplane just as you use your family car, providing that you obey all regulations.

According to FAA rules, a private pilot may, for compensation or hire, act as pilot in command of an aircraft in connection with any business or employment if the flight is only incidental to that business or employment and the aircraft does not carry passengers or property for compensation or hire. A holder of this license may share the operating expenses of a flight with his passengers. The word *share* here is very important. Technically, it means that your passengers cannot be required to pay for 100 percent of the expenses involved in a flight of which they are a part.

After you have obtained your student pilot's license, the work really begins. The serious seeker of the private license will do very little "enjoyment flying". All flying activity will be work . . . *hard* work. Stalls will be entered and recovered from time and again. Even during the required cross country flights, there is very little time for sightseeing, as flying charts must constantly be coordinated with the sightings of ground markers which indicate the adherence of the craft to the plotted course. Between flights, the student will be constantly practicing his course plotting abilities, along with memorizing the many rules and regulations. He may even attend a special weekend ground school to become more familiar with the material necessary to pass the written exam. This test may be taken at any time, as long as the various criteria are met.

Finally, the day will come when it's time for the FAA flight test. Nerves are often on edge, and the same assuredness which is often part of a first solo flight is simply not there. You know you're going to be flying with a stranger who will be judging your abilities to pilot an aircraft as a private license holder. He will be observing good traits as well as your bad. Again, comparison can be drawn between this and your first driver's test with a State Police Officer riding next to you.

To be eligible to be given the FAA flight test, an applicant must have passed the required written test, have the applicable instruction and aeronautical experience already described, and hold a current third class medical certificate. Additionally, the applicant must provide proof of age and have a written statement from a certificated flight instructor stating that he has given the applicant flight instruction in preparation for the flight test within sixty days preceding the date of application, and finds him competent to pass the test and to have satisfactory knowledge of the subject areas in which he is shown to be deficient by his FAA airman written test report.

The flight test itself starts on the ground with the student being required to plot a course between the FAA airport facility and a distant destination. Once in the air, the ability of an applicant for a private license is rated in several different areas including:

■ Executing procedures and maneuvers within the aircraft's performance capabilities and limitations, including use of the aircraft's systems.

■ Executing emergency procedures and maneuvers appropriate to the aircraft.

■ Piloting the aircraft with smoothness and accuracy.

■ Exercising judgment.

■ Applying his aeronautical knowledge.

■ Showing that he is the master of the aircraft, with the successful outcome of a procedure or maneuver never seriously in doubt.

Should the applicant fail any of the required pilot operations just outlined, the entire flight test has been failed. The applicant is not eligible for the certificate sought until he or she passes any pilot operations which have been failed. The FAA examiner or the applicant may discontinue the flight test at any time when the failure of a required pilot operation makes the applicant ineligible for the certificate or rating sought. If the test is discontinued, the applicant is entitled to credit for only those entire pilot operations which have been successfully performed.

If you should fail either the written or flight test, you must wait thirty days before you can be retested. However, in the case of a first failure, you may apply for retesting before the thirty days have expired by presenting a written statement from an authorized instructor certifying that he or she has given you flight or ground instruction and now finds you competent to pass the test. This applies to your *first* failure only.

Now that you have a bit of background on what is involved in obtaining a private pilot's license, perhaps some practicalities should be discussed. First of all, it is nearly impossible for the average student to be qualified to take the flight test after a minimum of forty hours flying time has been logged. Due to the hours required in certain aspects of flight training such as cross country flying, night flying, etc., you will probably find that when forty hours have been logged, you will still need an additional few hours in one of these specialized areas to have the minimum amount of time required for testing by the FAA. Fifty to fifty-five hours is a more practical goal to shoot for in taking your private pilot's flight test, but don't be surprised if log time exceeds sixty hours in some cases.

As was previously mentioned, many airport facilities offer package prices including ground school and flight instruction which will take you through to a private pilot's license. A phone call to the local airport in the author's home town produced the following prices (early 1981) on training plans:

Plan A - Ground school and flight training through solo....$700.00

Plan B - Ground school and flight training through private pilot's license...$1500.00

Plan C - Flight training from solo to completed cross country...$400.00

While prices will vary from area to area, it should be possible for persons in small communities to go all the way through the training course to a private pilot's license for less than $2000.00. Speaking in terms of very broad averages, a person who works regular hours and has a limited time to devote to flight training can usually qualify for the private license within a six month period. With a little more attention and practice, a student who is able to fly during the week may be licensed within two months. And if you really want to push it, you may even be the holder of a private pilot's license within a month. The unofficial record is 2½ weeks, but it certainly does not pay to rush into this, as certain reflex actions and instincts must be experienced over and over before they are really learned. It would be fair to say that a person who has never driven an automobile would probably not be able to get their license any faster than a person who had never flown an airplane, providing both students worked equally hard in getting each of the respective licenses.

SUMMARY

It is hoped that the purpose of this chapter has been fully realized by the reader. Flying is not an extremely difficult pursuit. At the same time, it is not easy. It requires strict adherence to rules and regulations, attention to operational details, and continued motivation. Flying airplanes is not dangerous; however, this pursuit can be terribly unforgiving of major mistakes. For this reason, the entire training program is based on how to avoid making these major mistakes and how to rectify them should they occur. Certainly, mistakes will be made by student and professional pilots alike. Fortunately, these mistakes are not often repeated and aren't major in scope in most instances.

Flying is quite enjoyable and does not require that the pilot be constantly observing instruments, the ground, the surrounding airspace and weather to the exclusion of all other normal trip aspects such as conversation with passengers, enjoying a sandwich while in flight, and even witnessing the beauty of a sunset. The good pilot learns to enjoy these aspects of the trip while still continuing to observe instruments, the ground, weather and surrounding airspace. In other words, the carrying out of these latter functions becomes instinctive, reflexive, and second nature. This is what makes flying fun, rewarding, and very safe.

Chapter 4

Single-Engine Fixed Gear Airplanes

The newcomer to flying is often quite overwhelmed by the many different types of aircraft available and by the multitude of models which abound in any one classification. For the purpose of this discussion, we will divide the various types of aircraft into three basic categories: single-engine planes with fixed gear, single-engine planes with retractable gear, and twin-engine aircraft. Each of these categories has its own special advantages as well as limitations.

This chapter will deal exclusively with many, but not all, of the newly manufactured single-engine fixed gear airplanes. These are the type most often flown by holders of a private pilot's license. The other types mentioned will be discussed in the following two chapters. Each plane will be pictured along with a brief description and manufacturers' specifications and performance data.

Single-engine fixed gear airplanes account for the majority of all planes in use today. These are basic airplanes, although many of them will have elaborate instrument packages, air conditioning, and many other special features. They can run from less than $20,000 to well over $100,000, depending upon the model chosen and the number of accessories purchased. Some are designed for basic training purposes, while others may be used for serious instrument training. Performance figures vary tremendously on these planes, with some having cruise speeds of around 100 miles per hour while others exceed 150 miles per hour. One type of plane in this category may be specifically designed for landing on dirt runways or even in open fields and is intended for bush flying and general utility operation. Another model by the same company will have a longer body, plush seats and be designed to carry four passengers in absolute comfort for great distances. The two types of planes may look as different as night and day, but they carry the same category rating, each having a single engine and fixed landing gear.

It is hoped the reader will be able to visit a local airport and examine first-hand many of the planes featured in this chapter. Manufacturers are obviously sold on their own products and play up each model's outstanding features; but to go back to an earlier statement, all planes have advantages and disadvantages. Only through hands-on experience can the potential aircraft buyer really learn all there is to know about these aspects of the aircraft.

PIPER SUPER CUB

The term "Piper Cub" has been used for many decades as a description for any light plane. Thousands have learned to fly in Piper Cubs. Some instructors still prefer this aircraft for training purposes and it finds much popularity in C.A.P. search applications.

The Piper Super Cub shown in Fig. 4-1 is a much-changed version of the original J-3 Cub which emerged in the early Forties. It is a heavier airplane, weighing in at 946 pounds empty. Its useful load is 804 pounds, which is very respectable for an aircraft of this size, and its fuel consumption is only 9 gallons per hour. It climbs out nearly 1,000 feet per minute and has a useful service ceiling of nearly 20,000 feet. Cruising range is excellent, exceeding 450 miles without refueling.

The Piper Super Cub is regularly used for many utility purposes. Law enforcement agencies, along with forest, fish, and game personnel, find this plane to be instrumental due to its ability to fly both low and slow. Inaccessible wilderness or jungle sites are often within reach of this very versatile aircraft.

The Super Cub may be outfitted with floats, as shown in Fig. 4-2, or even skis (Fig. 4-3). The Cub has always been a utility airplane and, even today, remains refreshingly uncomplicated. Simplified construction techniques and systems result in reliable performance with a minimum of maintenance.

The fuselage structure is made of welded steel tubing which is corrosion resistant. The wing framework consists of aluminum spars and ribs with aluminum sheeting used to form the leading edge. The Dacron fabric covering is not only fire-resistant and

Fig. 4-1. Piper Super Cub (courtesy Piper Aircraft Corp.).

durable but can easily be repaired in the field should minor damage occur.

Transporting two in tandem, the Piper Super Cub is neither very comfortable nor easy to fly. This latter trait is one which still makes it the choice of some flight instructors who feel students make better pilots when trained in an aircraft which must be constantly flown by the pilot. Most other training airplanes are relatively easy to fly and often do not acquaint the student with some situations which may be encountered in other types of airplanes. The Cub is not particularly comfortable because of its utility design and overall simplicity. Entering the cockpit can be a bit difficult and the noise factor is rather high, but as a "working" airplane, it offers many features which are hard to beat. Table 4-1 provides performance ratings and specifications.

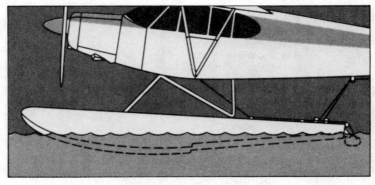

Fig. 4-2. Piper Super Cub outfitted with floats (courtesy Piper Aircraft Corp.).

Fig. 4-3. Piper Super Cub outfitted with skis (courtesy Piper Aircraft Corp.).

CESSNA 152

The Cessna Model 152 shown in Fig. 4-4 is reputed to be the number one training aircraft in the world today. The 152 is an update of the old Model 150, which is no longer manufactured. The 152 is still a lightweight two-seater and is the best selling airplane in the world today.

Offered for the first time in 1981 is the 152 Trainer, which includes the most frequently ordered avionics and accessories at a package price. Cessna states that the savings on a 152 Trainer

Table 4-1. Performance Data And Specifications
For Piper Super Cub (courtesy Piper Aircraft Corp.).

Wing Span: 35.3 ft.
Wing Area: 178.5 ft.^{2}
Wing Loading: 10 lbs./ft.^{2}
Length: 22.5 ft.
Height: 6.7 ft.
Engine: Lycoming 0-320, 150 bhp @ 2700 rpm
Fuel Capacity: 35.8 gal.
Empty Weight: 946 lbs.
Maximum Weight: 1750 lbs.
Maximum Useful Load: 804 lbs.
Baggage Weight: 50 lbs.
Speed, Max: 130 mph/113 kts.
Speed, Cruise @ 75% Power: 115 mph/100 kts.
Stall Speed Flaps Down: 43 mph/37 kts.
Rate Of Climb: 960 fpm.
Service Ceiling: 19,000 ft.
Takeoff Distance
    Ground Roll: 200 ft.
    Total Distance Over 50' Obstacle: 500 ft.
Landing Distance
    Ground Roll: 350 ft.
    Total Distance Over 50' Obstacle: 885 ft.

compared to buying individually selected items at list price is more than 20%. Standard with the 152 Trainer and optional on all other 152 models is a new cockpit intercom system which includes a lightweight handset and microphone. This hookup permits student/instructor conversations at normal voice levels. The system's volume control is located on the audio panel. Microphone switches on each control wheel allow radio transmissions outside the aircraft, and all communications can be monitored by student and instructor by using the intercom. Many other options are also included in the Trainer package which Cessna has designed in an attempt to reduce training costs.

Another model of the 152 is called the Aerobat and is specifically designed to teach and develop advanced pilot skills. It is certified for barrel rolls, spins, chandelles, lazy eights, Immelmanns, snap rolls, and other aerobatic maneuvers.

Each of the 152 models carries a comprehensive warranty which covers airframe, avionics, propeller, engine and accessories. Prices of the airplane at the factory range from a low of $21,350 for the basic 152 up to $28,600 for the 152 Aerobat. Table 4-2 provides complete performance data and specifications for the various models.

PIPER TOMAHAWK

The Piper Tomahawk shown in Fig. 4-5 is Piper's answer to the need for a low wing trainer. Its all-metal design is highlighted by a jet-age T-tail that positions the fixed horizontal stabilizer and interchangeable elevators in air which is undisturbed by the

Fig. 4-4. Cessna Model 152 (courtesy Cessna Aircraft Co.).

Table 4-2. Performance Data And Specifications
For Cessna Model 152 (courtesy Cessna Aircraft Corp.).

	152	Aerobat
Wing Span:	33 ft. 2 in.	33 ft. 2 in.
Wing Area:	159.5 ft.^{2}	159.5 ft.^{2}
Wing Loading:	10.5 lb/ft.^{2}	10.5 lb/ft.^{2}
Length:	24 ft. 1 in.	24 ft. 1 in.
Height:	8 ft. 6 in.	8 ft. 6 in.
Engine: Avco Lycoming 0-235-L2C: 110 bhp @ 2550 rpm.		
Propeller: Fixed pitch, 64 in. diameter.		
Fuel Capacity:	39 gal.	39 gal.
Oil Capacity:	7 qt.	7 qt.
Empty Weight:	1104 lb.	1140 lb.
Maximum Weight:	1670 lb.	1670 lb.
Maximum Useful Load:	571 lb.	535 lb.
Baggage Weight:	120 lb.	120 lb.
Speed, Max:	110 kts.	109 kts.
Speed, Cruise @ 75% Power:	107 kts.	106 kts.
Stall Speed		
Flaps Up:	48 kts.	48 kts.
Flaps Down:	43 kts.	43 kts.
Rate Of Climb:	715 fpm.	715 fpm.
Service Ceiling:	14,700 ft.	14,700 ft.
Takeoff Distance		
Ground Roll:	725 ft.	725 ft.
Total Distance Over 50′ Obstacle:	1340 ft.	1340 ft.
Landing Distance		
Ground Roll:	475 ft.	475 ft.
Total Distance Over 50′ Obstacle:	1200 ft.	1200 ft.

propeller's slipstream. This tends to make the flight noticeably quieter and more stable.

The Tomahawk landing gear is a full ten feet wide with a sturdy shock absorption action that compliments the built-in air cushion typical of a low wing airplane during landing. This two-seater is completely useable on sod fields for training with no modifications required.

A 112 horsepower Lycoming engine is used which has an economical 2,000 hour operating time before overhaul is required. Unlike other Piper single-engine aircraft, the Tomahawk has two doors for easier access to the cockpit.

This is one of the first really new trainers to be offered in many years, and there were some problems during the first year or so of production. However, the new models have been "de-bugged," so to speak, and the popularity of this new design is spreading rapidly. The one-piece wraparound windshield and rear window provide exceptional all-around visibility. This is certainly a plus regarding visual safety, with the pilot having nearly a 360 degree unobstructed view.

The Piper Tomahawk excels in the low operating expense category. Piper estimates a cost of approximately $18.97 per hour

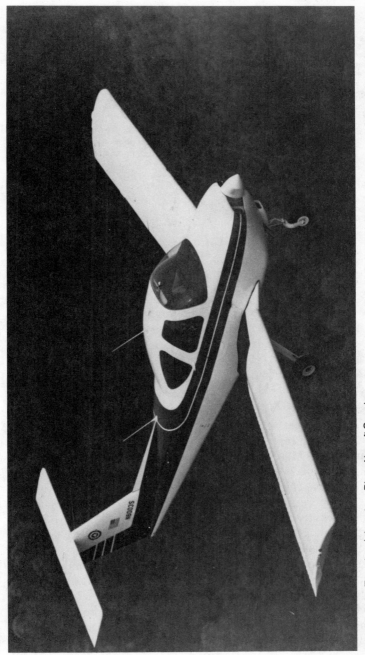

Fig. 4-5. Piper Tomahawk (courtesy Piper Aircraft Corp.).

51

```
Wing Span: 34 ft.
Wing Area: 124.7 ft.²
Wing Loading: 13.39 lb/ft.².
Length: 23.1 ft.
Height: 9.06 ft.
Cabin Width: 42.0 in.
Cabin Height: 50.5 in.
Headroom, Front: 35.0 in.
Engine: Lycoming 0-235-L2C, 112 bhp @2600 rpm
Fuel Capacity: 32 gal.
Oil Capacity: 6 qts.
Empty Weight: 1109 lbs.
Maximum Weight: 1670 lbs.
Maximum Useful Load: 561 lbs.
Baggage
     Weight: 100 lbs.
     Volume: 20 ft.³
Speed, Max: 109 kts.
Speed, Cruise @75% Power: 108 kts.
Stall Speed
     Flaps Up: 52 kts.
     Flaps Down: 49 kts.
Rate Of Climb: 718 fpm.
Service Ceiling: 13,000 ft.
Takeoff Distance
     Ground Roll: 820 ft.
     Total Distance Over 50' Obstacle: 1460 ft.
   Landing Distance
     Ground Roll: 707 ft.
     Total Distance Over 50' Obstacle: 1544 ft.
```

Table 4-3. Performance Data and Specifications For Piper Tomahawk (courtesy Piper Aircraft Corp.).

of operation. At a purchase price of approximately $28,000, the Tomahawk is certainly in line with the going rate for comparable trainers from other companies. For those desiring an economical low wing two-seater, the Tomahawk offers many attractive features. Table 4-3 provides a complete chart of performance data and physical specifications.

CESSNA SKYHAWK

The Cessna Skyhawk shown in Fig. 4-6 might be thought of as the standard vehicle of light airplane owners who prefer the high wing design. More than 33,000 of these planes have been sold and the new models offer an increased useful load, a new engine, improved handling, and a new avionics cooling system.

Ramp weight of the Skyhawk has been increased 100 pounds. This allows for 89 pounds more useful load for a total of 993 pounds. With four 170 pound people aboard and nearly 75 pounds of baggage, there is enough useful load for 40 gallons of fuel.

The new engine is a 160 horsepower Lycoming which provides a maximum speed of 123 knots (141 mph). Engine accessories include a standard oil cooler and full flow oil filter.

The Skyhawk is a comfortable airplane which provides a good combination of comfort, performance, and fuel efficiency. More fuel can be carried in this new model with the introduction of an

Fig. 4-6. Cessna Skyhawk (courtesy Cessna Aircraft Co.).

53

extra long range option which features a wet wing fuel tank system containing 62 usable gallons. Optional 50 gallon tanks are also available in addition to the standard 40 gallon tank.

Skyhawk interior and exterior styling is available in many coordinated colors. The standard interior includes solid vinyl seat trim, Corona fabric seat inserts, solid vinyl sidewall areas, Horizon carpet and seat belts. The instrument panel can be selected in black or shadow gray.

The Skyhawk can be purchased with a "II" package, which includes a list of the most commonly ordered avionics and accessories at a factory-installed price. A "Nav/Pac" option adds a second 300 Nav/Com, a 300 Automatic Direction Finder (ADF), and a 300 transponder to the "II" configuration.

A 2,000 hour TBO (time before overhaul) rated engine can be covered on a pro-rated basis by Cessna Aircraft. The basic Skyhawk starts at slightly less than $34,000, while a Skyhawk II with Nav/Pac tops the basic line at about $42,500. Table 4-4 provides a complete listing of performance and specifications on this model aircraft.

CESSNA HAWK XP

The Cessna Hawk XP (Fig. 4-7) is a modified version of the Skyhawk and offers about 10 knots more cruising speed and generally better performance than the previously discussed model. Rate of climb is 870 feet per minute at sea level compared with about 700 feet per minute for the standard Skyhawk. The useful load is 1,012 pounds for a wide choice of flexibility. As was the case with the Skyhawk, the Hawk XP is available either as a land plane or as a float plane. For improved performance, the Hawk XP utilizes a fuel-injected 195 horsepower engine. Other features include a 76 inch diameter, constant speed propeller. Cost for the basic Hawk XP is $41,850, while the XP II with Nav/Pac and additional factory installed equipment is priced at $50,790. Table 4-5 provides performance data and specifications for the landplane and floatplane models.

BEECHCRAFT SKIPPER

The Beechcraft Skipper shown in Fig. 4-8 is the Beech Aircraft Corporation's entry into the T-tail trainer category. At a basically equipped price of about $24,000, the Skipper features a 115 horsepower Lycoming engine and 72-inch aluminum alloy fixed pitch propeller. Left and right cabin entrance doors make for ease

Fig. 4-7. Cessna Hawk XP (courtesy Cessna Aircraft Co.).

of entry and exit. Other standard equipment includes toe-operated brakes, electrically operated flaps, nose wheel steering and rudder trim system.

The landing gear is of the fixed tricycle type with a steerable, self-centering nose wheel. It also has a 120 pound baggage capacity which is quite sizeable for a plane in this category.

A respectable rate of climb of 720 fpm is complimented by a 105 knot (121 mph) cruise speed at 80% power. It carries a useful load of 577 pounds and boasts a range of between 375 and 475 miles with adequate reserve, depending upon altitude and power setting.

The T-tail arrangement adds to the stability of the airplane in flight and also makes for quieter operations. Designed with the student pilot in mind, the main landing gear is of the tubular spring variety with an oleo shock absorber nose gear. The plane can easily withstand the normal abuses which take place in student training exercises. Table 4-6 provides performance data and specifications for this low wing trainer.

BEECHCRAFT SUNDOWNER

The Beechcraft Sundowner shown in Fig. 4-9 is a four-place single-engine aircraft of low wing design offering good general specifications and performance for many types of operation. Two

Table 4-4. Performance Data and Specifications For Cessna Skyhawk (courtesy Cessna Aircraft Co.).

	Landplane	Floatplane
Wing Span:	35 ft. 10 in.	35 ft. 10 in.
Wing Area:	174 ft.²	174 ft.²
Wing Loading:	13.8 lb/ft.²	12.7 lb/ft.²
Length:	26 ft. 11 in.	26 ft. 8 in.
Height:	8 ft. 9½ in.	11 ft. 11 in.
Engine: Lycoming 0-320-D2J, 160 bhp @ 2700 rpm	Fixed pitch,	Fixed pitch,
Propeller:	75 in. diameter	80 in. diameter.
Fuel Capacity:	43 gal.	43 gal.
Oil Capacity:	8 qt.	8 qt.
Empty Weight:	1414 lb.	1593 lb.
Maximum Weight:	2407 lb.	2227 lb.
Maximum Useful Load:	993 lb.	634 lb.
Baggage Weight:	120 lb.	120 lb.
Speed, Max:	123 kts.	96 kts.
Speed, Cruise @ 75% Power:	120 kts.	95 kts.
Stall Speed		
Flaps Up:	51 kts.	48 kts.
Flaps Down:	46 kts.	44 kts.
Rate Of Climb:	700 fpm.	740 fpm.
Service Ceiling:	13,000 ft.	15,000 ft.
Takeoff Distance		
Ground Roll:	890 ft.	1400 ft.
Total Distance Over 50′ Obstacle:	1825 ft.	2160 ft.
Landing Distance		
Ground Roll:	540 ft.	590 ft.
Total Distance Over 50′ Obstacle:	1280 ft.	1345 ft.

Fig. 4-8. Beechcraft Skipper (courtesy Beech Aircraft Corp.).

28.6 gallon fuel tanks offer a cruising range with 45 minute reserve of over 650 statute miles at economical power settings. Cruise speed at 84% power is 123 knots (141 mph) at 4,500 feet. Its rate of climb at sea level is a respectable 792 fpm at full power.

The Sundowner offers a 19.5 cubic foot baggage compartment. Additionally, 3.8 cubic feet are available on a built-in accessory shelf. A full 270 pounds of baggage may be loaded into this compartment. The overall useful load of the aircraft is 950 pounds.

Normal takeoff distance at sea level is only 1,130 feet, making this plane suitable for short field uses. The wide spacing of the main landing gear makes this plane very stable in rough field conditions as well.

The Beechcraft Sundowner contains a 4-cylinder Lycoming engine rated at a constant 180 horsepower. Standard flight instruments include an air speed indicator, altimeter, magnetic compass and stall warning horn. The engine instrument complement is made up of a recording tachometer, ammeter, fuel quantity gauges, oil pressure and oil temperature gauge and a fuel pressure gauge. A 76-inch fixed pitch aluminum alloy propeller tops off the aircraft.

Ease of ground fixed operation is obtained with fixed tricycle gear and a steerable, self-centering nose wheel. Disc shock absorbers are mounted on all wheel struts for smoother taxiing and landing ease. Standard hydraulic brakes are controlled by toe-operated linkage to the rudder pedals.

At a standard equipment price of $39,350, the Beechcraft Sundowner is attractive to many purchasers of aircraft in this category. It is a tough four-seater which offers many general use features from all types of runways. Table 4-7 provides performance data and specifications for this low wing trainer.

CESSNA SKYLANE

The Cessna Skylane shown in Fig. 4-10 has long been known as the standard workhorse of the Cessna line. Labeled as the standard-bearer for Cessna's high performance single-engine models, its roomy, comfortable cabin makes it a very attractive package to many light plane buyers. The Skylane's reputation for comfort, speed, range and payload, plus landing ease has made it a valuable commodity for many years.

The Cessna Skylane's performance includes a 144 knot (166 mph) cruise, 1254 pound useful load, and range extending to 1255

Table 4-5. Performance Data and Specifications
For Cessna Hawk XP (courtesy Cessna Aircraft Co.).

	Landplane	Floatplane
Wing Span:	35 ft. 10 in.	35 ft. 10 in.
Wing Area:	174 ft.^{2}	174 ft.^{2}
Wing Loading:	14.7 lb/ft.^{2}	14.7 lb/ft.^{2}
Length:	27 ft. 2 in.	26 ft. 10 in.
Height:	8 ft. 9½ in.	12 ft. 5 in.
Engine: Teledyne - Continental 10-360-KB, 195 bhp @ 2600 rpm		
Propeller: Constant speed, 2 blade, 76 in. dia.	Constant speed, 2 blade, 80 in. dia.	
Fuel Capacity:	52 gal.	52 gal.
Oil Capacity:	9 qt.	9 qt.
Empty Weight:	1546 lb.	1808 lb.
Maximum Weight:	2558 lb.	2558 lb.
Maximum Useful Load:	1012 lb.	750 lb.
Baggage Weight:	200 lb.	200 lb.
Speed, Max:	133 kts.	118 kts.
Speed, Cruise @ 75% Power:	130 kts.	116 kts.
Stall Speed		
Flaps Up:	52 kts.	50 kts.
Flaps Down:	47 kts.	44 kts.
Rate Of Climb:	870 fpm.	870 fpm.
Service Ceiling:	17,000 ft.	15,500 ft.
Takeoff Distance		
Ground Roll:	800 ft.	1135 ft.
Total Distance Over 50′ Obstacle:	1360 ft.	1850 ft.
Landing Distance		
Ground Roll:	635 ft.	675 ft.
Total Distance Over 50′ Obstacle:	1345 ft.	1390 ft.

statute miles. It is equipped with a 230 horsepower Continental engine and a constant speed propeller is standard. Baggage allowance is 200 pounds, and it exhibits a highly respective rate of climb at sea level in excess of 1,000 fpm.

The flap position control has a new, highly visible plastic indicator for improved appearance and easy reading. The new models boast wing flap electrical circuitry which has been redesigned to reduce the number of wires and connections. This simpler design requires less maintenance and provides for a more dependable system.

The Cessna Skylane can be depended upon to carry four adult passengers and ample baggage for each with comfort, speed and a highly useful effective range. This high performance package provides excellent takeoff and landing even at small runways and on dirt fields. It's an all-around airplane providing convenience, comfort and excellent hauling ability for utility uses.

The Skylane is available with many different options, with the basic airplane selling for about $45,000. The Skylane II with Nav/Pac instrumentation sells for about $10,000 more. The

Wing Span: 32 ft. 9 in.
Wing Area: 146 ft.^{2}
Wing Loading: 16.78 lb/ft.^{2}
Length: 25 ft. 9 in.
Height: 8 ft. 3 in.
Cabin Width: 44 in.
Cabin Height: 48 in.
Headroom
    Front: 37.5 in.
    Rear: 35.5 in.
Fuel Capacity: 57.2 gal.
Oil Capacity: 8 qt.
Empty Weight: 1505 lbs.
Maximum Weight: 2450 lbs.
Maximum Useful Load: 950 lbs.
Baggage
    Weight: 270 lbs.
    Volume: 19.5 ft.^{3}
Speed, Max: 141 mph/123 kts.
Speed, Cruise @ 75% Power: 136 mph/119 kts.
Stall Speed, Flaps Down: 59 mph/51 kts.
Rate Of Climb: 792 fpm.
Service Ceiling: 12,600 ft.
Takeoff Distance
    Ground Roll: 1,130 ft.
    Total Distance Over 50' Obstacle: 1,955 ft.
Landing Distance
    Ground Roll: 703 ft.
    Total Distance Over 50' Obstacle: 1,484 ft.

Table 4-6. Performance Data and Specifications For Beechcraft Skipper (courtesy Beech Aircraft Corp.).

Nav/Pac option incorporates commonly ordered avionics and accessories which provide savings due to the factory installation. Many Skylanes are equipped for full IFR flight. Due to the electronic equipment, a complete airplane can easily approach or exceed the $100,000 category. Table 4-8 provides performance data and specifications for the Skylane. Figure 4-11 shows the instrument panel and seating configuration.

PIPER WARRIOR II

The Piper Warrior II shown in Fig. 4-12 is an excellent all-around airplane for those individuals who prefer the low wing design. It offers good cruise speed, comfort, passenger and baggage capacity, and range. It is also an economical airplane to fly with its 160 horsepower Lycoming engine providing a 127 knot (146) mph cruise at 75% power. The interior is roomy; and behind the rear seat, there is a 24 cubic foot luggage compartment that can hold up to 200 pounds. Individual ventilation systems mounted in the overhead console offer fingertip control. A wide selection of

Fig. 4-9. Beechcraft Sundowner (courtesy Beech Aircraft Corp.).

**Table 4-7. Performance Data and Specifications
For Beechcraft Sundowner (courtesy Beech Aircraft Corp.).**

	Baggage
Wing Span: 30 ft.	Weight: 120 lbs.
Wing Area: 129.8 ft.^{2}	Volume: 20.1 ft.^{3}
Wing Loading: 12.9 lbs/ft.^{2}	Speed, Max: 122 mph/106 kts.
Length: 24 ft.	Speed, Cruise @ 75% Power: 121 mph/105 kts.
Height: 6 ft. 11 in.	Stall Speed, Flaps Down: 54 mph/47 kts.
Cabin Width: 42.75 in.	Rate Of Climb: 720 fpm.
Cabin Height: 48.75 in.	Service Ceiling: 12,900 ft.
Headroom, Front: 37.5 in.	Takeoff Distance
Fuel Capacity: 29 gal.	Ground Roll: 780 ft.
Oil Capacity: 6 qt.	Total Distance Over 50' Obstacle: 1,280 ft.
Empty Weight: 1103 lbs.	Landing Distance
Maximum Weight: 1675 lbs.	Ground Roll: 670 ft.
Maximum Useful Load: 577 lbs.	Total Distance Over 50' Obstacle: 1,313 ft.

standard and deluxe interior fabrics provide the owner with many interior possibilities.

The Warrior II is an improved version of the old Piper Cherokee, which has been popular for many years. With pricing in the $40,000 to $50,000 range, it is certainly right in the competition with high wing planes offering comparable performance features. Piper estimates the per hour operating expense to be approximately $28.41. This is based partially upon a fuel consumption of 7.77 gph (gallons per hour) at $1.75 per gallon.

The Warrior II has a 2,000 TBO engine, so figuring an average usage of 300 hours per year, a major overhaul won't be needed for almost seven years. Like other planes in this category, this aircraft can be flown out of small runways and dirt fields. The widetrack oleo strut landing ear offers much versatility in rough field touchdowns. Table 4-9 provides performance data and specifications for this aircraft.

PIPER ARCHER II

The Piper Archer II shown in Fig. 4-13 offers a luxurious interior along with clean lines and an engine rated at 180 horsepower during takeoff, 178 horsepower continuous. It is a simple airplane with a fixed pitch propeller, seating for four persons, and many extra safety features. Yard-wide doors offer much in the area of passenger convenience. The four contoured reclining seats and a relatively spacious interior add up to a very comfortable means of transportation over long distances. At economy cruise speed, this aircraft has an effective range of over 1,200 miles, which includes a 45 minute fuel reserve. Figuring an

Fig. 4-10. Cessna Skylane (courtesy Cessna Aircraft Co.).

**Table 4-8. Performance Data and Specifications
For Cessna Skylane (courtesy Cessna Aircraft Co.).**

Wing Span: 35 ft. 10 in.
Wing Area: 174 ft.^{2}
Wing Loading: 16.9 lb/ft.^{2}
Length: 28 ft.
Height: 9 ft. 3 in.
Engine: Teledyne Continental 0-470-U, 230 bhp @ 2400 rpm
Propeller: Constant speed, 2 blade, 82 in. dia.
Fuel Capacity: 92 gal.
Oil Capacity: 12 qt.
Empty Weight: 1706 lb.
Maximum Weight: 2950 lb.
Maximum Useful Load: 1254 lb.
Baggage Weight: 200 lb.
Speed, Max: 148 kts.
Speed, Cruise @ 75% Power: 144 kts.
Stall Speed
    Flaps Up: 56 kts.
    Flaps Down: 50 kts.
Rate Of Climb: 1010 fpm.
Service Ceiling: 16,500 ft.
Takeoff Distance
    Ground Roll: 705 ft.
    Total Distance Over 50' Obstacle: 1350 ft.
Landing Distance
    Ground Roll: 590 ft.
    Total Distance Over 50' Obstacle: 1350 ft.

average fuel consumption of a little over 8 gph at $1.75 per gallon, the overall hourly operating expense should fall slightly under $30.00. This includes prorated costs for inspection and maintenance, engine and prop overhaul, and avionics maintenance. This plane should average approximately 16 statute miles per gallon at 65% cruise power.

The Archer II is a good performer with a cruise speed of 129 knots (148 mph) at 75% power. Among the many standard instruments and indicators are the altimeter, magnetic compass, tachometer, speed indicator, annunciator panel , and roto trim position indicator. The cabin comfort system includes the heater, windshield defrosters, cabin exhaust vent, four cabin fresh air vents, and provision for air conditioning.

The Archer provides a very respectable range, a useful load of 1,137 pounds, and a rate of climb of 735 fpm. The four reclining seats are an excellent comfort feature and are available in many fabric colors.

The 2,000 TBO Lycoming engine will give the average user many years of operation before a complete engine overhaul becomes necessary. In the option line, the Archer will allow you to choose from a full range of top quality avionics packages from Piper. Most buyers opt for an autopilot with heading hold and navigation coupling. The factory installation of avionics options allow for sizeable savings for the buyer.

Piper advertises the Archer as the four-place luxury single that's not a drain on the wallet. It sells at the factory in the $50,000 to $60,000 price range with a reasonable amount of radio/navigation equipment. Table 4-10 provides performance data and specifications for this aircraft.

PIPER DAKOTA

It can be seen from the picture of the Piper Dakota shown in Fig. 4-14 that the manufacturer follows the same proven design for

Fig. 4-11. Cessna Skylane instrument panel and seating configuration (courtesy Cessna Aircraft Co.).

all airplanes in this category. As we move up the line, the Dakota fills a very important spot in being an aircraft which offers excellent useful load, coupled with high performance and long range. This could be considered the workhorse of the Piper line, which packs a 235 horsepower Lycoming engine. This six cylinder design has the standard 2,000 hour capability before major overhaul.

The Dakota cruises at 144 knots (166 mph) and has the best rate of climb in its class at 1,100 fpm. It excels on takeoff, clearing a 50 foot obstacle in only 1,216 feet at sea level. The broad expanse of a swept-back fin and rudder, the long-span ailerons and one-piece stabilator deliver balanced control for outstanding handling.

Economically speaking, the Dakota is very miserly on fuel for this class of aircraft, with a consumption of 12.7 gph at 75% power. It also offers 24 cubic feet of luggage area and will carry four adults in comfort and style. Many interior decor options are available and the 1981 exterior paint scheme features horizontal stripes of blue and red on a white background.

Deluxe interior features include crushed velour, deep pile carpeting, and attractive curtains. The overhead console offers high capacity ventilation for added creature comforts. A new heavy duty brake option may be ordered for those pilots who anticipate short field operations with maximum loads. The useful load of the Dakota is 1,392 pounds.

The Dakota is also available in a turbocharged version which provides additional performance at high altitudes. The normally aspirated Dakota is priced within the $70,000 to $80,000 range. Its performance and specifications are listed in Table 4-11.

PIPER SARATOGA AND TURBO SARATOGA

Based upon the old Cherokee Six, the Piper Saratoga and Turbo Saratoga shown in Fig. 4-15 is a six-place single-engine aircraft offering the capabilities of many light twins. This aircraft features a wide body and large, two-section cargo/passenger door arrangement which allows for the transport of reasonably large items. The rear passenger seat may be removed to convert the entire interior into a cavernous cargo hold. Piper advertises the fact that you could even load a piano through the two big back doors.

The Saratoga certainly offers as many conveniences for passenger comfort as it does for cargo transporting efficiency. There is a deluxe new interior treatment which features comforta-

Fig. 4-12. Piper Warrior II (courtesy Piper Aircraft Corp.).

Wing Span: 35 ft.
Wing Area: 170 ft.^{2}
Wing Loading: 13.7 lb/ft.^{2}
Length: 23.8 ft.
Height: 7.3 ft.
Cabin Width: 41.5 in.
Cabin Height: 49.0 in.
Headroom
    Front: 36 in.
    Rear: 36 in.
Engine: Lycoming 0-320-D3G, 160 bhp @ 2700 rpm.
Propeller: Fixed pitch, 74 in. dia.
Fuel Capacity: 48 gal.
Oil Capacity: 8 qt.
Empty Weight: 1353 lbs.
Maximum Weight: 2325 lbs.
Maximum Useful Load: 972 lbs.
Baggage
    Weight: 200 lbs.
    Volume: 24 ft.^{3}
Speed, Max: 127 kts.
Speed, Cruise @ 75% Power: 123 kts.
Stall Speed
    Flaps Up: 50 kts.
    Flaps Down: 44 kts.
Rate Of Climb: 710 fpm
Takeoff Distance
    Ground Roll: 975 ft.
    Total Distance Over 50' Obstacle: 1490 ft.
Landing Distance
    Ground Roll: 595 ft.
    Total Distance Over 50' Obstacle: 1115 ft.

Table 4-9. Performance Data and Specifications For Piper Warrior II (courtesy Piper Aircraft Corp.).

ble knit fabric. Contoured seats are topped by tapered headrests, and the interior can be custom-tailored for individual preferences.

The two models are basically identical in appearance. The normally aspirated Saratoga has a range of over 1,100 statute miles with a 45 minute fuel reserve. Total fuel capacity is 102 gallons. Cruising at 75% power is a healthy 150 knots (173 mph) under the power of a standard 6 cylinder 300 horsepower Lycoming engine with a 2,000 hour TBO.

For added performance, there is a Turbocharged Saratoga which will fly higher and faster than its normally aspirated counterpart. Top speed of the Turbo is 182 knots (205) mph, climbing out at over 1,000 feet per minute. 75% cruise power can be maintained up to an altitude of 20,000 feet. A built-in oxygen system is available with the Turbo Saratoga with outlets at each seat. Another option is the three-bladed prop which reduces cabin noise while developing peak performance on takeoff. Both models have a useful load of over 1,600 pounds.

Prices for these models exceed the $100,000 mark. The normally aspirated Saratoga is in the $103,000 range, while the Turbo Saratoga will sell for slightly over $110,000. Table 4-12 provides data and specifications for both planes.

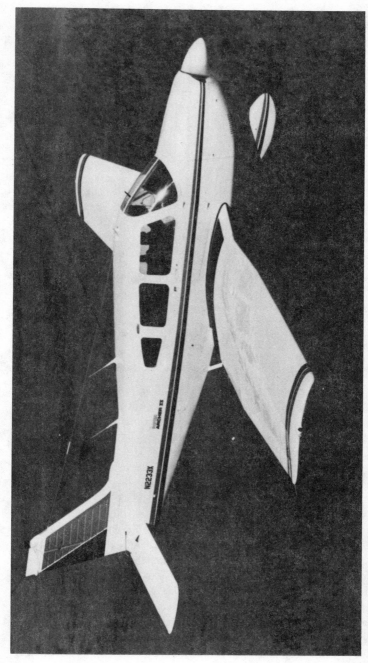

Fig. 4-13. Piper Archer II (courtesy Piper Aircraft Corp.).

```
Wing Span: 35 ft.
Wing Area: 170 ft.²
Wing Loading: 15.0 lb/ft.²
Length: 23.8 ft.
Height: 7.3 ft.
Cabin Width: 41.5 in.
Cabin Height: 49.0 in.
Headroom
    Front: 36 in.
    Rear: 36 in.
Engine: Lycoming 0-360-A4M, 178 bhp @ 2650 rpm
Propeller: Fixed pitch, 76 in. dia.
Fuel Capacity: 48 gal.
Oil Capacity: 8 qt.
Empty Weight: 1413 lbs.
Maximum Weight: 2550 lbs.
Maximum Useful Load: 1137 lbs.
Baggage
    Weight: 200 lbs.
    Volume: 26 ft.
Speed, Max: 129 kts.
Speed, Cruise @ 75% Power: 126 kts.
Stall Speed
    Flaps Up: 55 kts.
    Flaps Down: 49 kts.
Rate Of Climb: 735 fpm
Takeoff Distance
    Ground Roll: 870 ft.
    Total Distance Over 50' Obstacle: 1625 ft.
Landing Distance
    Ground Roll: 925 ft.
    Total Distance Over 50' Obstacle: 1390 ft.
```

Table 4-10. Performance Data and Specifications For Piper Archer II (courtesy Piper Aircraft Corp.).

CESSNA STATIONAIR 6

The Cessna Stationair 6 shown in Fig. 4-16 may be used for carrying up to six people or, in a utility configuration, it is capable of hauling big payloads into short landing strips. For those customers who desire higher performance, a turbocharged model is also available. This latter plane is more appropriate for operating in and out of high altitude airports. The Stationair 6 is also certified for water operation as well as land and may be fitted with aircraft floats for this purpose.

The normally aspirated model has a useful load of 1,685 pounds, cruises at 147 knots (169 mph) at 75% power at an altitude of 6,500 feet, and has a range of 783 statute miles with 88 gallons of usable fuel. The turbocharged version allows the versatility of high-altitude operations, cruising at 167 knots (192 mph) at 20,000. At this altitude and power setting, the Turbo Stationair 6 has a range of 737 statute miles.

Both Stationair 6 models have pilot-side doors for entry to pilot and copilot seats, and large double doors on the right side provide excellent access to passenger seats or for loading cargo. A

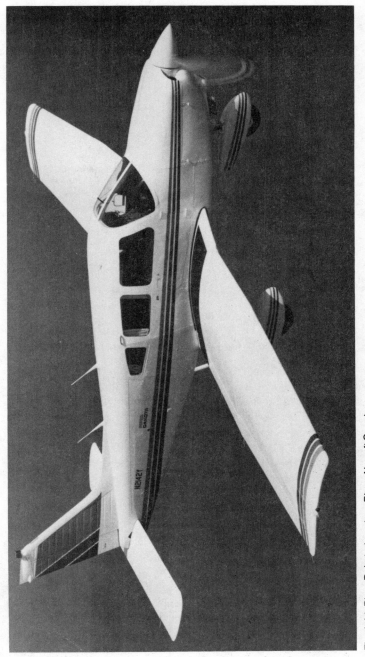

Fig. 4-14. Piper Dakota (courtesy Piper Aircraft Corp.).

Wing Span: 35.4 ft.
Wing Area: 170 ft.^{2}
Wing Loading: 17.6 lb/ft.^{2}
Length: 24.7 ft.
Height: 7.2 ft.
Cabin Width: 41.5 in.
Cabin Height: 49.0 in.
Headroom
    Front: 36 in.
    Rear: 36 in.
Engine: Lycoming O-540-J3A5D,
    235 bhp @ 2400 rpm
Propeller: Hartzell constant speed,
    2 blade, 80 in. dia.
Fuel Capacity: 72 gal.
Oil Capacity: 12 qt.
Empty Weight: 1608 lb.
Maximum Weight: 3000 lb.
Maximum Useful Load: 1392 lb.
Baggage
    Weight: 200 lb.
    Volume: 26 ft.^{3}
Speed, Max: 148 kts.
Speed, Cruise % 75% Power: 139 kts.
Stall Speed
    Flaps Up: 65 kts.
    Flaps Down: 56 kts.
Rate Of Climb: 1110 fpm
Service Ceiling: 17,500 ft.
Takeoff Distance
    Ground Roll: 886 ft.
    Total Distance Over 50' Obstacle: 1216 ft.
Landing Distance
    Ground Roll: 825 ft.
    Total Distance Over 50' Obstacle: 1725 ft.

Table 4-11. Performance Data and Specifications For Piper Dakota (courtesy Piper Aircraft Corp.).

choice of interiors can be selected in six different colors. Seat back recline locks make seat back movement quick and easy. An optional writing desk can even be ordered for the backs of fully articulating front seats. It folds to a compact position when not in use. Stereo entertainment is even available with an optional six-place stereo entertainment center specifically designed for aircraft use. This option includes AM/FM radio, cassette stereo player and six headphone jacks. It features audio interrupt to allow radio transmissions to be heard.

Utility options include an ambulance kit, photographic provisions, a skydiving kit and provisions for glider towing. The airplanes can be ordered with provisions for the installation of floats, and the Turbo Stationair 6 for amphibian floats.

Prices of the airplane at the factory in Wichita, Kansas range from $58,750 for the standard equipped Stationair 6 to nearly $80,000 for a Turbo Stationair 6 with Nav-Pac options. Table 4-13 provides performance data and specifications for the normally aspirated Stationair 6. Table 4-14 provides the same information for the Turbo model.

Fig. 4-15. Piper Saratoga (courtesy Piper Aircraft Corp.).

73

Table 4-12. Performance Data and Specifications For Piper Saratoga and Turbo Saratoga (courtesy Piper Aircraft Corp.).

	Saratoga	Turbo Saratoga
Wing Span:	36.2 ft.	36.2 ft.
Wing Area:	178.3 ft.^{2}	178.3 ft.^{2}
Wing Loading:	20.2 lb/ft.^{2}	20.2 lb/ft.^{2}
Length:	27.7 ft.	28.2 ft.
Height:	8.2 ft.	8.2 ft.
Cabin Width:	49.0 in.	49.0 in.
Cabin Height:	49.0 in.	49.0 in.
Headroom		
Front:	36 in.	36 in.
Rear:	36 in.	36 in.
Engine: Lycoming, 300 bhp @ 2700 rpm Lycoming, 300 bhp @ 2700 rpm		
Propeller: Hartzell constant speed, 2 blade, 80 in. dia.		
Fuel Capacity:	102 gal.	102 gal.
Oil Capacity:	12 qt.	12 qt.
Empty Weight:	1940 lbs.	2003 lbs.
Maximum Weight:	3600 lbs.	3600 lbs.
Maximum Useful Load:	1675 lbs.	1614 lbs.
Baggage		
Weight:	200 lbs.	200 lbs.
Volume:	24.3 ft.^{3}	24.3 ft.^{3}
Speed, Max:	152 kts.	178 kts.
Speed, Cruise 75% Power:	148 kts.	160 kts.
Stall Speed		
Flaps Up:	62 kts.	62 kts.
Flaps Down:	58 kts.	58 kts.
Rate Of Climb:	990 fpm	1075 fpm
Service Ceiling:	14,100 ft.	20,000 + ft.
Takeoff Distance		
Ground Roll:	1183 ft.	1110 ft.
Total Distance Over 50' Obstacle:	1759 ft.	1590 ft.
Landing Distance		
Ground Roll:	732 ft.	732 ft.
Total Distance Over 50' Obstacle:	1612 ft.	1725 ft.

CESSNA STATIONAIR 8

No other single-engine airplane offers a payload seating capability of the Cessna Stationair 8, an elongated version of the Stationair 6. The aircraft shown in Fig. 4-17 also offers optional six-place club seating with a conference area and substantially more leg and shoulder room. Included are high headrests for all seats. A writing table and refreshment bar are also offered as options.

The Stationair 8 exceeds the payload capability of many twin-engine planes and is also available in a turbocharged version. The large cabin is supplemented by a 9.5 cubic foot forward baggage compartment that can hold 120 pounds. The turbo version can also be equipped with an easily attachable cargo pack, adding a 300 pound capacity.

Standard usable fuel is 54 gallons with a range at 75% power and 6,500 feet cruising at 143 knots (165 mph) of 403 statute miles. With the optional 73 gallon fuel tanks, range is 604 statute miles. These figures apply to the normally aspirated model.

Fig. 4-16. Cessna Stationair 6 (courtesy Cessna Aircraft Co.).

75

	Landplane	Floatplane
Wing Span:	35 ft. 10 in.	35 ft. 10 in.
Wing Area:	174 ft.^{2}	174 ft.^{2}
Wing Loading:	20.7 lb/ft.^{2}	20.1 lb/ft.^{2}
Length:	28 ft. 3 in.	29 ft. 8 in.
Height:	9 ft. 3½ in.	14 ft. 1½ in.
Engine: Teledyne Continental 10-520-F, 285 bhp @ 2700 rpm.		
Propeller: Constant speed, 3 blade, 80 in. dia.		
Fuel Capacity:	92 gal.	92 gal.
Oil Capacity:	12 qt.	12 qt.
Empty Weight:	1927 lb.	2264 lb.
Maximum Weight:	3600 lb.	3500 lb.
Maximum Useful Load:	1685 lb.	1248 lb.
Baggage Weight:	180 lb.	180 lb.
Speed, Max:	156 kts.	138 kts.
Speed, Cruise @ 75% Power:	147 kts.	132 kts.
Stall Speed		
Flaps Up:	62 kts.	56 kts.
Flaps Down:	54 kts.	51 kts.
Rate Of Climb:	920 fpm	925 fpm
Service Ceiling:	14,800 ft.	13,900 ft.
Takeoff Distance		
Ground Roll:	900 ft.	1835 ft.
Total Distance Over 50' Obstacle:	1780 ft.	2820 ft.
Landing Distance		
Ground Roll:	735 ft.	780 ft.
Total Distance Over 50' Obstacle:	1395 ft.	1675 ft.

The Turbo Stationair 8 cruises at 161 knots (185 mph) at 20,000 feet at 80% power. Range with the standard tank is 345 statute miles, 547 miles with the optional 73 gallon tanks.

Both Stationair 8 models can be ordered with the Cessna II packages of popular accessories and avionics at factory-installed savings. List price for the normally aspirated Stationair 8 with standard equipment is $68,450. a standard Turbo Stationair 8 lists for $76,200. Table 4-15 provides complete specifications and performance data for both models.

CESSNA SKYWAGON 180 AND 185

Tailwheel airplanes are still preferred by many pilots, especially those who regularly operate from unimproved landing strips. The Cessna Skywagons are designed as working airplanes and offer agricultural options to equip them for aerial application or ag pilot training. The option includes a 151-gallon fan-driven Sorenson spray system with electric spray valve, deflector cable plus windshield and landing gear wire cutters. Jet-flo polyurethane paint is used for extra corrosion protection.

Both models feature excellent utility performance and are available with provision for installation of floats, amphibian floats or skis. Versatility is further enhanced with options for aerial photography or stretcher installation.

Table 4-14. Performance Data and Specifications
For Turbo Cessna Stationair 6 (courtesy Cessna Aircraft Co.).

	Floatplane	Amphibian	
Wing Span:	35 ft. 10 in.	35 ft. 10 in.	
Wing Area:	174 ft.^{2}	174 ft.^{2}	
Wing Loading:	20.7 lb/ft.^{2}	20.7 lb/ft.^{2}	
Length:	29 ft. 8 in.	29 ft. 5 in.	
Height:	14 ft. 1½ in.	12 ft. 6½ in.	
Engine: Teledyne Continental TS10-520-M, 285 bhp @ 2600 rpm			
Propeller: Constant speed, 3 blade, 80 in. dia.			
Fuel Capacity:	92 gal.	92 gal.	
Oil Capacity:	13 qt.	13 qt.	
Empty Weight:	2338 lb.	2630 lb.	
Maximum Weight:	3616 lb.	3616 lb.	
Maximum Useful Load:	1278 lb.	986 lb.	
Baggage Weight:	180 lb.	180 lb.	
Speed, Max:	155 kts.	150 kts.	
Speed, Cruise @ 75% Power:	147 kts.	141 kts.	
Stall Speed			
Flaps Up:	57 kts.	57 kts.	
Flaps Down:	52 kts.	52 kts.	
Rate Of Climb:	835 fpm	810 fpm	
Service Ceiling:	25,600 ft.	25,100 ft.	
Takeoff Distance		Land	Water
Ground Roll:	1810 ft.	945 ft.	1810 ft.
Total Distance Over 50' Obstacle:	2790 ft.	1840 ft.	2790 ft.
Landing Distance			
Ground Roll:	845 ft.	750 ft.	845 ft.
Total Distance Over 50' Obstacle:	1750 ft.	1410 ft.	1750 ft.

	Standard	
Wing Span:	35 ft. 10 in.	
Wing Area:	174 ft.^{2}	
Wing Loading:	20.7 lb/ft.^{2}	
Length:	28 ft. 3 in.	
Height:	9 ft. 3½ in.	
Engine: Teledyne Continental TS10-520-M, 285 bhp @ 2600 rpm		
Propeller: Constant speed, 3 blade, 80 in. dia.		
Fuel Capacity:	92 gal.	
Oil Capacity:	13 qt.	
Empty Weight:	2003 lb.	
Maximum Weight:	3616 lb.	
Maximum Useful Load:	1613 lb.	
Baggage Weight:	180 lb.	
Speed, Max:	174 kts.	
Speed, Cruise @ 75% Power:	167 kts.	
Stall Speed		
Flaps Up:	62 kts.	
Flaps Down:	54 kts.	
Rate Of Climb:	1010 fpm	
Service Ceiling:	27,000 ft.	
Takeoff Distance		
Ground Roll:	835 ft.	
Total Distance Over 50' Obstacle: 1640 ft.		
Landing Distance		
Ground Roll:	735 ft.	
Total Distance Over 50' Obstacle: 1395 ft.		

Fig. 4-17. Cessna Stationair 8 (courtesy Cessna Aircraft Co.).

Powered by a six-cylinder 230 horsepower Continental engine, the 180 Skywagon has a maximum speed of 148 knots (170 mph), an 1,100 fpm rate of climb at sea level and a maximum useful load of 1,166 pounds. Range with 84 gallons of usable fuel, 75% power at 8,000 feet, is 904 statute miles.

**Table 4-15. Performance Data and Specifications
For Cessna Stationair 8 (courtesy Cessna Aircraft Co.).**

Wing Span: 35 ft. 10 in.
Wing Area: 174 ft.^{2}
Wing Loading: 21.8 lb/ft.^{2}
Length: 32 ft. 2 in.
Height: 9 ft. 7 in.
Engine: Teledyne Continental 10-520-F, 285 bhp @ 2700 rpm
Propeller: Constant speed, 3 blade, 80 in. dia.
Fuel Capacity: 61 gal.
Oil Capacity: 12 qt.
Empty Weight: 2105 lb.
Maximum Weight: 3800 lb.
Maximum Useful Load: 1707 lb.
Baggage Weight: 300 lb.
Speed, Max: 150 kts.
Speed, Cruise @ 75% Power: 143 kts.
Stall Speed
    Flaps Up: 65 kts.
    Flaps Down: 58 kts.
Rate Of Climb: 810 fpm
Service Ceiling: 13,300 ft.
Takeoff Distance
    Ground Roll: 1100 ft.
    Total Distance Over 50' Obstacle: 1970 ft.
Landing Distance
    Ground Roll: 765 ft.
    Total Distance Over 50' Obstacle: 1500 ft.

Fig. 4-18. Cessna Skywagon 180 (courtesy Cessna Aircraft Co.).

The 185 Skywagon is powered by a six-cylinder Continental engine rated at 300 horsepower for takeoff and 285 horsepower for continuous operation. Maximum speed is 154 knots (177) mph; rate of climb is 1,075 fpm; and range with 84 gallons of usable fuel at 75% power and 7,000 feet is 742 statute miles.

The 180 Skywagon is shown in Fig. 4-18 and lists for $41,975 with standard equipment. The 185 Skywagon shown in Fig. 4-19 lists for about $10,000 more. Table 4-16 provides performance data and specifications for the 180 Skywagon both in the landplane and skiplane versions. Table 4-17 provides the same information for the 185 Skywagon.

Performance of the 185 in the floatplane, amphibian and agricultural utility categories is provided by the data in Table 4-18.

Fig. 4-19. Cessna Skywagon 185 (courtesy Cessna Aircraft Co.).

Table 4-16. Performance Data and Specifications For Cessna 180 Skywagon (courtesy Cessna Aircraft Co.).

	Landplane	Skiplane
Wing Span:	35 ft. 10 in.	35 ft. 10 in.
Wing Area:	174 ft.^{2}	174 ft.^{2}
Wing Loading:	16.1 lb/ft.^{2}	16.1 lb/ft.^{2}
Length:	25 ft. 7½ in.	27 ft. 9½ in.
Height:	7 ft. 9 in.	7 ft. 9 in.
Engine: Teledyne Continental 0-470-U, 230 bhp @ 2400 rpm		
Propeller: Constant speed, 2 blade, 82 in. dia.		
Fuel Capacity:	88 gal.	
Oil Capacity:	12 qt.	
Empty Weight:	1644 lb.	1786 lb.
Maximum Weight:	2800 lb.	2800 lb.
Maximum Useful Load:	1166 lb.	1024 lb.
Baggage Weight:	170 lb.	170 lb.
Speed, Max:	148 kts.	129 kts.
Speed, Cruise @ 75% Power:	142 kts.	124 kts.
Stall Speed		
Flaps Up:	53 kts.	
Flaps Down:	48 kts.	
Rate Of Climb:	1100 fpm	910 fpm
Service Ceiling:	17,700 ft.	14,700 ft.
Takeoff Distance		
Ground Roll:	625 ft.	
Total Distance Over 50' Obstacle:	1205 ft.	
Landing Distance		
Ground Roll:	480 ft.	
Total Distance Over 50' Obstacle.	1365 ft.	

Table 4-17. Performance Data And Specifications For Cessna 185 Skywagon (courtesy Cessna Aircraft Co.).

	Landplane	Skiplane
Wing Span:	35 ft. 10 in.	35 ft. 10 in.
Wing Area:	174 ft.^{2}	174 ft.^{2}
Wing Loading:	14.3 lb/ft.^{2}	14.3 lb/ft.^{2}
Length:	25 ft. 7½ in.	27 ft. 9½ in.
Height:	7 ft. 9 in.	7 ft. 9 in.
Engine: Teledyne Continental 10-520-0, 285 bhp @ 2700 rpm		
Propeller: Constant speed, 3 blades, 80 in. dia.		
Fuel Capacity:	88 gal.	
Oil Capacity:	12 qt.	
Empty Weight:	1688 lb.	1830 lb.
Maximum Weight:	3350 lb.	
Maximum Useful Load:	1674 lb.	1532 lb.
Baggage Weight:	170 lb.	
Speed, Max:	154 kts.	136 kts.
Speed, Cruise @ 75% Power:	147 kts.	131 kts.
Stall Speed		
Flaps Up:	56 kts.	
Flaps Down:	49 kts.	
Rate Of Climb:	1075 fpm	860 fpm
Service Ceiling:	17,900 ft.	15,500 ft.
Takeoff Distance		
Ground Roll:	825 ft.	
Total Distance Over 50' Obstacle:	1430 ft.	
Landing Distance		
Ground Roll:	610 ft.	
Total Distance Over 50' Obstacle:	1400 ft.	

**Table 4-18. Performance Data And Specifications
For Cessna 185 Skywagon in Floatplane Amphibian
And Agricultural Utility Categories (courtesy Cessna Aircraft Co.).**

	Floatplane	Amphibian	AG Option
Wing Span:	35 ft. 10 in.	35 ft. 10 in.	35 ft. 10 in.
Wing Area:	174 ft.^{2}	174 ft.^{2}	174 ft.^{2}
Wing Loading:	19.1 lb/ft.^{2}	18.8 lb/ft.^{2}	19.3 lb/ft.^{2}
Length:	27 ft.	27 ft. 6 in.	25 ft. 7½ in.
Height:	12 ft. 2 in.	12 ft. 8 in.	7 ft. 10½ in.
Engine: Teledyne Continental 10-520-D, 285 bhp @ 2700 rpm Propeller: Constant speed, 3 blade, 80 in. dia.			
Fuel Capacity:	88 gal.	88 gal.	88 gal.
Oil Capacity:	12 qt.	12 qt.	12 qt.
Empty Weight:	1990 lb.	2245 lb.	1910 lb.
Maximum Weight:	3320 lb.	3265 lb.	3350 lb.
Maximum Useful Load:	1342 lb.	1032 lb.	(151 gal. spray)
Baggage Weight:	170 lb.	170 lb.	
Speed, Max:	140 kts.	135 kts.	129 kts.
Speed, Cruise @ 75% Power:	133 kts.	129 kts.	121 kts.
Stall Speed			
Flaps Up:	56 kts.	55 kts.	56 kts.
Flaps Down:	52 kts.	51 kts.	49 kts.
Rate Of Climb:	960 fpm	950 fpm	845 fpm
Service Ceiling:	16,400 ft.	16,100 ft.	13,400 ft.
Takeoff Distance			
Ground Roll:	1430 ft.	780 ft. land/1125 ft. water	850 ft.
Total Distance Over 50' Obstacle:	2125 ft.	1325 ft. land/1710 ft. water	1520 ft.
Landing Distance			
Ground Roll:	830 ft.	570 ft. land/775 ft. water	610 ft.
Total Distance Over 50' Obstacle:	1565 ft.	1240 ft. land/1480 ft. water	1400 ft.

SUMMARY

This chapter has featured many of the single-engine, fixed gear aircraft currently being manufactured in the United States. A good sampling of what is available to the potential aircraft buyer is represented here, but many other planes may also be found. Quite a few of these will be discovered on the used plane market and will be forerunners of the new models discussed here. Product checks with other manufacturers will reveal more to the reader about *all* of the models currently on the American market. Generally speaking, each aircraft type will exhibit special advantages and disadvantages. Two planes from different manufacturers may be nearly identical in one area of specifications or performance and completely different in another. For this reason, an aircraft buyer will often get detailed specifications from several manufacturers and weigh all of the advantages and disadvantages before deciding on what is best for his or her particular needs. The models discussed in this chapter represent aircraft types which form the vast majority of all planes owned and/or operated by private pilots.

Chapter 5

Single-Engine
Retractable Gear Airplanes

To be most efficient in flight, airplanes must be designed with clean, aerodynamic lines. The general bullet shape of most airplane fuselages indicates the designers' adherence to this principle. Unfortunately, necessities such as landing gear compromise these smooth lines and introduce drag into the airframe. This drag limits the airplane's speed, which also directly affects many other performance criteria such as fuel consumption, range, etc.

Since it is impossible to do away with the landing gear, the next best thing is to draw it up into the fuselage or wings when not in use. In this manner, aerodynamic lines are maintained while in flight, with the landing gear being lowered shortly before touchdown.

Plane for plane, *retractable gear designs* are much more efficient and provide greatly improved performance due to the reduced aerodynamic drag. They generally fly faster, farther, and at a savings in fuel when compared with fixed gear models. A good example of this can be effectively demonstrated by comparing the specifications and performance data of the Cessna Skylane RG (the RG indicates retractable gear) and the standard Skylane with fixed gear. Using engines of nearly identical horsepower, the RG model has a maximum speed at sea level of 160 knots compared with 148 knots in the Skylane with fixed gear. The cruise speed of the Skylane RG is about 180 mph at 7,500 feet, while the cruise speed of the fixed gear Skylane under the same conditions is 166 mph. Looking at the rate of climb statistics, with retractable gear, the

Skylane climbs at 1,140 fpm compared with 1,010 fpm for the fixed gear model.

Of course, the mechanical complexities of retractable gear designs add considerably to the list price of a standard equipped plane. However, the advantages that can be had by retracting the gear may make the more expensive model actually cheaper over the operational life of the plane. Again, the purposes for which the plane is to be used will determine whether or not a retractable gear design is the best choice.

BEECHCRAFT SIERRA

The Beechcraft Sierra shown in Fig. 5-1 is a four to six-place low wing, retractable gear, all metal airplane powered by a Lycoming fuel injected engine rated at 200 horsepower. A constant speed propeller is included as standard equipment. Maximum speed at sea level for this model is a hefty 142 knots (163 mph) with a range of 790 statute miles at economy cruise settings.

The Sierra has retractable tricycle gear with a steerable, self-centering nose wheel. Disc shock absorbers on all wheel struts are designed for smooth taxiing and landing characteristics. Hydraulic brakes are actuated by toe-operated controls on the rudder pedals. As is the case with most retractables, there is a gear-up warning horn which sounds should a landing be attempted before the gear is dropped into place. This horn is controlled by the throttle.

The Beechcraft Sierra is at home on runways at international airports or even on a tiny grass strip near some rural community. Normal ground run on takeoff is slightly less than 1,100 feet. Takeoff attitude configuration calls for 15 degrees of flaps. Normal landing distance with 35 degrees of flaps is 816 feet. Both of these published performance features assume a sea level runway, zero wind and standard temperatures.

For passenger comfort, the Sierra offers left and right cabin entrance doors and a left side baggage door. The interior panels disguise quite a bit of soundproofing to shut out engine and wind noise. Each plane is equipped with full upholstering, including wall-to-wall carpeting. Adjustable front seats have three-position reclining backs (for and aft), and there is a two-place rear bench seat. Also as standard equipment, Beechcraft includes inertia reel shoulder harnesses and lap belts for all seats.

Special features which are included as standard equipment with this aircraft are a baggage area which is accessible in flight, emergency locater transmitter, centralized door latch, and a tow bar and tie down rings.

The Beechcraft Sierra lists for $53,900 as a standard-equipped retractable gear airplane. Table 5-1 provides performance data and specifications for this model.

MOONEY 201

One mile per hour for each horsepower has always been a goal to shoot for among designers of high performance airplanes. The Mooney 201 shown in Fig. 5-2 is a retractable gear speedster, producing a top speed of over 200 mph while using a 200 horsepower Lycoming engine. Top speed is 201 mph or 174 knots. This is the reason Mooney Aircraft Corporation named this model the 201.

For those individuals desiring an economical performance airplane, the 201 may fill the bill. It can cruise along at 195 mph while burning only 10 gallons of aviation fuel per hour. This is at a cruising altitude of 8,000 feet. This breaks down to a thrifty 18.1 miles per gallon. Economy cruise power settings offer even better mpg ratings.

The Mooney 201 handles four full-sized adults in comfort in a cabin measuring 43.5 inches from elbow to elbow. The contoured seats come in a choice of rich vinyls, handsome genuine leather, as well as tasteful patterned fabric.

The new Mooney 201 features what the manufacturer calls the New Dimension panel. It is designed for the serious pilot with all important flight instruments and controls within easy sight and reach. The 201 comes with a choice of nine autopilot systems and fourteen different avionics packages.

For a high performance airplane, the Mooney 201 has a very quiet cabin. Wind noise and "prop beating" have been reduced due to the aerodynamic design of the plane, thus allowing it to attain the speed it does with only a 200 horsepower engine.

The 201 features all electric gear and the gear may be lowered at initial air speeds of up to 150 mph. Backing up this electrical system is a spring-loaded gear extension system which is easily accessible in the center of the cabin. The large aerodynamically refined windshield provides excellent visibility and smooth air flow and a new airline-style overhead ventilation system is more efficient and much quieter than ordinary systems, providing a greater degree of comfort for pilot and passengers alike.

Fig. 5-1. Beechcraft Sierra (courtesy Beech Aircraft Corp.).

```
Wing Span: 32 ft. 9 in.
Wing Area: 146 ft.²
Wing Loading: 18.84 bl/ft.²
Length: 25 ft. 9 in.
Height: 8 ft. 1 in.
Cabin Width: 44 in.
Cabin Height: 48 in.
Headroom
      Front: 37.5 in.
      Rear: 35.5 in.
Fuel Capacity: 57.2 gal.
Oil Capacity: 8 qt.
Empty Weight: 1701 lb.
Maximum Weight: 2750 lb.
Maximum Useful Load: 1057 lb.
Baggage
      Weight: 270 lb.
      Volume: 19.5 ft.³
Speed, Max: 163 mph/142 kts.
Speed, Cruise @ 75% Power: 158 mph/137 kts.
Stall Speed
      Flaps Up: 75 mph/65 kts.
      Flaps Down: 69 mph/60 kts.
Rate Of Climb: 927 fpm
Service Ceiling: 15,385 ft.
Takeoff Distance
      Ground Roll: 1063 ft.
      Total Distance Over 50' Obstacle: 1561 ft.
Landing Distance
      Ground Roll: 816 ft.
      Total Distance Over 50' Obstacle: 1462 ft.
```

Table 5-1. Performance Data and Specifications For Beechcraft Sierra (courtesy Beech Aircraft Corp.).

One unavoidable setback in a plane of this type is usually a lower TBO rating on the engine. A high performance airplane usually has tighter engine cowling; therefore, the powerplant operates at a higher temperature. This decreases the number of hours the engine may be operated before a major overhaul is necessary. The Mooney 201 TBO is 1,600 hours, whereas an airplane of more standardized performance would probably have a 2,000 hour TBO when using the same engine. Of course, the additional speed and fuel economy can often offset this situation, and for many people, the high performance Mooney 201 is an ideal answer to their needs for a fast, economical four-place airplane. Table 5-2 provides specifications and performance data for the 201, which lists in a standard equipped configuration for about $52,000.

MOONEY 231

The Mooney Turbo 231 is a turbocharbed version of the model 201 just discussed. Its name was derived in the same way as its normally aspirated counterpart, in that top speed of the Turbo is 231 mph . . . and this is at maximum gross weight. It can easily cruise along at 210 mph, while still getting over 18 miles out of

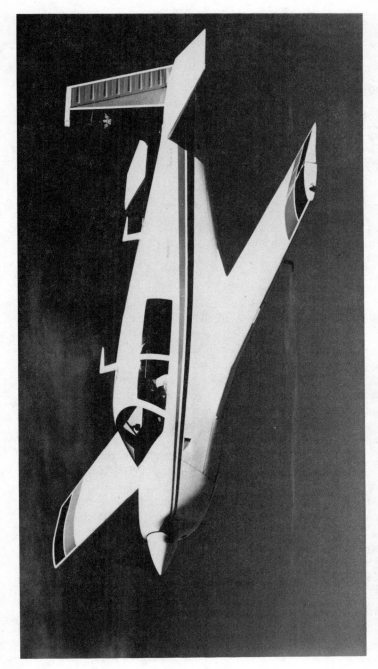

Fig. 5-2. Mooney 201 (courtesy Mooney Aircraft Corp.).

87

Wing Span: 35 ft.
Wing Area: 167 ft.^{2}
Wing Loading: 16.4 lb/ft.^{2}
Length: 24 ft. 8 in.
Height: 8 ft. 4 in.
Engine: Lycoming 10-360-A3B6D, 200 bhp
Fuel Capacity: 64 gal.
Empty Weight: 1640 lb.
Maximum Weight: 2740 lb.
Maximum Useful Load: 1100 lb.
Baggage Weight: 120 lb.
Speed, Max: 201 mph/174 kts.
Speed, Cruise @ 75% Power: 195 mph/169 kts.
Stall Speed Flaps Down: 61 mph/53 kts.
Rate Of Climb: 1030 fpm
Service Ceiling: 18,800 ft.

Table 5-2. Performance Data and Specifications For Mooney 201 (courtesy Mooney Aircraft Corp.).

each gallon of fuel. It has an operational ceiling of 24,000 feet, giving it the capability of climbing above a lot of adverse weather conditions.

At 8,000 feet with 75% power, the 231 provides an impressive 191 mph at a very economical fuel consumption rate. The turbocharged engine is a Teledyne-Continental 210 horsepower model which makes this plane ideal for operations in and out of high altitude airports.

Specifications are similar to the 201 in that the fuselage is designed with room for four adults. 43.5 inches of cabin width is also provided, as with the former plane. The handling characteristics of the Turbo 231 have some pleasant surprises. A balanced pitch system with an even large elevator provides positive rotation on takeoff. Aerodynamically sculptured wing tips reduce vortex drag and aileron back pressure.

Shown in Fig. 5-3, it can be seen that it is very difficult to distinguish the 231 from the 201 when in flight. The Turbo Mooney lists for only $57,775, about $6,000 higher than the 201. This makes it one of the least expensive turbocharged planes on today's market. Without a doubt, from a fuel consumption standpoint, the two Mooneys are among the best around. Table 5-3 provides a list of specifications and performance data for this model.

CESSNA CUTLASS RG

The four-place Cessna Cutlass RG shown in Fig. 5-4 was introduced in 1980 by the Cessna Aircraft Company and accounted for almost 38% of the four-place retractable market during that year. It offers a clean design, and its 180 horsepower powerplant

Fig. 5-3. Mooney 231 (courtesy Mooney Aircraft Corp.).

89

Wing Span: 36 ft. 1 in.
Wing Area: 174.8 ft.^{2}
Wing Loading: 16.6 lb .ft.^{2}
Length: 25 ft. 5 in.
Height: 8 ft. 3 in.
Engine: Teledyne-Continental TS10-360-GB, 210 bhp
Fuel Capacity: 73 gal.
Empty Weight: 1,800 lb.
Maximum Weight: 2,900 lb.
Maximum Useful Load: 1,100 lb.
Baggage Weight: 120 lb.
Speed, Max: 231 mph/201 kts.
Speed, Cruise @ 75% Power: 210 mph/182 kts.
Stall Speed Flaps Down: 66 mph
Rate Of Climb: 1080 fpm
Service Ceiling: 24,000 ft.

with constant speed propeller combine for a cruise speed of 140 knots (161) mph at only 10 gallons per hour. Range at that cruise power with maximum useable fuel of 62 gallons is 829 statute miles.

One of the areas in which the Cutlass RG excels is in load-carrying capability. Takeoff weight is 2,650 pounds and useful load is over 1,100 pounds. Two full-size doors plus a baggage door make loading relatively easy, and the baggage area is certified for 200 pounds.

Gear operating speed is 161 mph and the first 10 degrees of flap can be lowered at 130 knots, allowing for rapid descent. The Cutlass RG features standard equipment such as an avionics cooling system, a new type of oil pressure gauge, and an improved navigation antenna. Avionics cooling is by a fan operated from the master switch. It draws cabin air, reducing the risk of moisture ingestion and eliminating the need for a cowling scoop on the fuselage. The fan delivers approximately four cubic feet per minute of cooling air to one section of the panel while two cubic feet of air per minute are delivered to the transponder and DME sections. A 2,000 hour TBO engine is standard.

Table 5-4 provides performance figures and specifications for the Cutlass RG, which lists for $52,400. Factory options are available, including avionics which can push the list price to nearly $63,000.

CESSNA SKYLANE RG AND TURBO SKYLANE RG

The Cessna Skylane has long been known as the workhorse of the Cessna line. This is the fixed gear version, which has been

Fig. 5-4. Cessna Cutlass RG (courtesy Cessna Aircraft Co.).

Table 5-4. Performance Data and Specifications For Cessna Cutlass RG (courtesy Cessna Aircraft Co.).

Wing Span: 35 ft. 10 in.
Wing Area: 174 ft.^{2}
Wing Loading: 15.2 lb/ft.^{2}
Length: 27 ft. 5 in.
Height 8 ft. 9½ in.
Engine: Avco Lycoming 0-360-F1A6, 180 bhp @ 2700 rpm
Propeller: Constant speed, 3 blade, 76.5 in. dia.
Fuel Capacity: 66 gal.
Oil Capacity: 9 qt.
Empty Weight: 1555 lb.
Maximum Weight: 2658 lb.
Maximum Useful Load: 1103 lb.
Baggage Weight: 200 lb.
Speed, Max: 145 kts.
Speed, Cruise @ 75% Power: 140 kts.
Stall Speed
    Flaps Up: 54 kts.
    Flaps Down: 50 kts.
Rate Of Climb: 800 fpm
Service Ceiling: 16,800 ft.
Takeoff Distance
    Ground Roll: 1060 ft.
    Total Distance Over 50' Obstacle: 1775 ft.
Landing Distance:
    Ground Roll: 625 ft.
    Total Distance Over 50' Obstacle: 1340 ft.

around for years, so Cessna decided to make a good thing even better by giving the Skylane retractable gear and, later, turbocharging. Air conditioning is even available with cool air being routed to each seat position by means of individual air outlets from flush-mounted overhead ducts. Air induction for the unit is through external louvres and no cowling scoop is required.

The Turbo Skylane RG has an optional anti-icing system. This plane is not certified for flight into known icing conditions, but the optional de-icer is often chosen for added safety. It includes propeller and windshield anti-icing, heated pitot and stall warning, plus an ice detection light.

Both models retain the big, powerful feel of a Skylane and add the speed and fuel efficiency of a retractable. Interior styling includes individual high-back aft seats for greater passenger comfort, a choice of many interior options, and large sun visors to keep the passenger area cool.

The Cessna RG shown in Fig. 5-5 can cruise at 156 knots (180 mph) for 972 statute miles, and the useful load is 1,362 pounds. The Turbo Skylane RG cruises at 173 knots (199 mph) at 20,000 feet for

Fig. 5-5. Cessna Skylane RG (courtesy Cessna Aircraft Co.).

**Table 5-5. Performance Data and Specifications
For Cessna Skylane RG (courtesy Cessna Aircraft Co.).**

Wing Span: 35 ft. 10 in.
Wing Area: 174 ft.^{2}
Wing Loading: 17.8 lb/ft.^{2}
Length: 28 ft. 7½ in.
Height: 8 ft. 11 in.
Engine: Avco Lycoming 0-540-JEC5D, 235 bhp @ 2400 rpm
Propeller: Constant speed, 2 blade, 82 in. dia.
Fuel Capacity: 92 gal.
Oil Capacity: 9 qt.
Empty Weight: 1750 lb.
Maximum Weight: 3112 lb.
Maximum Useful Load: 1362 lb.
Baggage Weight: 200 lb.
Speed, Max: 160 kts.
Speed, Cruise @ 75% Power: 156 kts.
Stall Speed
　　Flaps Up: 54 kts.
　　Flaps Down: 50 kts.
Rate Of Climb: 1140 fpm
Service Ceiling: 14,300 ft.
Takeoff Distance
　　Ground Roll: 820 ft.
　　Total Distance Over 50' Obstacle: 1570 ft.
Landing Distance
　　Ground Roll: 600 ft.
　　Total Distance Over 50' Obstacle: 1320 ft.

949 statute miles and has a useful load of 1,321 pounds. Both models are available with factory-installed avionics packages and accessories. Prices for the airplane start at $58,750 for the Skylane RG. This will climb to about $70,000 with one of the avionics packages. The Turbo Skylane RG lists at $65,500 in the standard equipped version. A price of $75,955 is placed on the plane with factory-installed avionics. Table 5-5 provides complete specifications and performance data for the Skylane RG, which uses a 2,000 hour TBO 235 horsepower Lycoming engine. Table 5-6 provides the same performance data for the Turbo Skylane RG.

PIPER ARROW AND TURBO ARROW

Years ago, Piper Aircraft Corporation came out with a retractable version of their popular Cherokee. It was called the Arrow and gave Piper afficionados the opportunity to buy a retractable plane more along the lines of the Cherokee without having to go to the larger Commanche, which was the smallest retractable Piper manufactured before the Arrow. The Piper Arrow was immediately accepted and continues to be most popular even today, although many changes have been made in the meantime.

This low wing plane, shown in Fig. 5-6, features T-tail styling, good cruising speed and a respectable range of over 1,000 miles. There's plenty of head, shoulder and leg room for four adults, and the Arrow can honestly be described as having a luxurious cabin for a four-place single.

The Arrow is noted for its luggage room which allows for a 24 cubic foot capacity. Gross weight of the normally aspirated version is 2,750 pounds, 1,123 pounds of which is useful load.

With a 200 horsepower Lycoming engine, the normally aspirated Arrow cruises at 143 knots (165 mph), and carries over a half ton of fuel, baggage, and passengers. The turbocharged 200 horsepower Continental engine on the Turbo Arrow provides full-rated takeoff power from airports at high elevations. The same power is available at 6,000 feet as at sea level. This plane provides 75% cruising power up to 19,000 feet, where the top speed is over 200 mph. At 65% cruise power, fuel consumption is less than 11

Table 5-6. Performance Data And Specifications For Cessna Turbo Skylane RG (courtesy Cessna Aircraft Co.).

Wing Span: 35 ft. 10 in.
Wing Area: 174 ft.^{2}
Wing Loading: 17.8 lb/ft.^{2}
Length: 28 ft. 7½ in.
Height 8 ft. 11 in.
Engine: Turbocharged Lycoming 0-540-L3C5D, 235 bhp @ 2400 rpm
Propeller: Constant speed, 2 blade, 82 in. dia.
Fuel Capacity: 92 gal.
Oil Capacity: 9 qt
Empty Weight: 1791 lb.
Maximum Weight: 3112 lb.
Maximum Useful Load: 1321 lb.
Baggage Weight: 200 lb.
Speed, Max: 187 kts.
Speed Cruise @ 75% Power: 173 kts.
Stall Speed
    Flaps Up: 54 kts.
    Flaps Down: 50 kts.
Rate Of Climb: 1040 fpm
Service Ceiling: 20,000 ft.
Takeoff Distance
    Ground Roll: 820 ft.
    Total Distance Over 50′ Obstacle: 1570 ft.
Landing Distance
    Ground Roll: 600 ft.
    Total Distance Over 50′ Obstacle: 1320 ft.

gallons per hour. A three-bladed prop is available as an option for smoother and quieter operations.

Both models are useful for operations from short runways and unimproved fields. Their wide-spaced main landing gear provides good ground stability in less than ideal conditions.

Table 5-7 provides specifications and performance data for the Arrow and Turbo Arrow. The four-cylinder Lycoming engine used in the Arrow has a 1,600 hour TBO and the Turbo Arrow Continental six-cylinder engine is rated for an 1,800 hour TBO. Standard equipped price of the Arrow is about $83,000, with the turbocharged version selling for nearly $90,000. Piper calculates the hourly operating expense for the normally aspirated Arrow at $38.13, while the Turbo Arrow operates for slightly over $43.00 per hour.

CESSNA CENTURION AND TURBO CENTURION

Long known as the "flagship" of Cessna's single-engine aircraft line, the Centurion shown in Fig. 5-7 is a most comfortable airplane for business travel, combining high performance with a most commodious cabin. Customers can order air conditioning, color radar, and a myriad of other avionics devices. An optional electric generator is also available on the Turbo Centurion. The Centurion actually competes with many twin-engine aircraft in performance and comfort while maintaining the operational economy of a single-engine model.

Air conditioning for these models provides a system with individual air outlets for each seat position and twin blowers for maximum air distribution. The air is circulated through flush-mounted overhead ducting. A de-icing system is available for all models. Other interior trappings can include an optional writing desk with articulating front seats. It folds neatly into the seat back for storage. A stereo entertainment system can also be ordered and will accommodate headphones for up to a full six passengers.

Interior and exterior styling is very elegant. Hanover wool fabric is offered as the standard fabric for seats and sidewalls. Numerous options, including leather, are available to suit individual tastes. Front seats on the two Centurions have an additional 3½ inches of travel over older models for ease of entry and exit.

The Centurion and Turbo Centurion have increased oxygen system flexibility over previous models, with an optional oxygen system installed over the wheel well. Capacity is 75.5 cubic feet, and the system weighs 21 pounds less than the previous overhead system used by Cessna.

Fig. 5-6. Piper Arrow (courtesy Piper Aircraft Corp.).

Table 5-7. Performance Data and Specifications For Piper Arrow IV and Turbo Arrow IV (courtesy Piper Aircraft Corp.).

	ARROW IV	TURBO ARROW IV
Wing Span:	35.4 ft.	35.4 ft.
Wing Area:	170 ft.^{2}	170 ft.^{2}
Wing Loading:	16.2 lb/ft.^{2}	17.1 lb/ft.^{2}
Length:	27.0 ft.	27.3 ft.
Height:	8.3 ft.	8.3 ft.
Cabin Width:	41.5 in.	41.5 in.
Cabin Height:	49.0 in.	49.0 in.
Headroom		
Front:	36 in.	36 in.
Rear:	36 in.	36 in.
Engine: Lycoming 10-360-C1C6, 196 bhp ⅜ 2650	Continental TS10-360-FB, 200 bhp @ 2575	
Propeller: McCauley constant speed	Hartzell constant speed	
Fuel Capacity:	72 gal.	72 gal.
Oil Capacity:	8 qt.	8 qt.
Empty Weight:	1637 lb.	1692 lb.
Maximum Weight:	2750 lb.	2900 lb.
Maximum Useful Load:	1113 lb.	1208 lb.
Baggage		
Weight:	200 lb.	200 lb.
Volume:	26 ft.^{3}	26 ft.^{3}
Speed, Max:	149 kts.	178 kts.
Speed, Cruise @ 75% Power:	135 kts.	168 kts.
Stall Speed		
Flaps Up:	58 kts.	66 kts.
Flaps Down:	53 kts.	61 kts.
Rate Of Climb:	831 fpm	940 fpm
Service Ceiling:	16,200 ft.	20,000 + ft.
Takeoff Distance		
Ground Roll:	1025 ft.	1110 ft.
Total Distance Over 50' Obstacle:	1600 ft.	1620 ft.
Landing Distance		
Ground Roll:	615 ft.	645 ft.
Total Distance Over 50' Obstacle:	1525 ft.	1555 ft.

With 89 gallons of usable fuel, the normally aspirated Centurion can cruise at 171 knots (197 mph) at 6,500 feet for 927 statute miles. Useful load is 1,679 pounds. The turbocharged version cruises at 199 knots (229 mph) at 22,000 feet for a range of 869 statute miles. Useful load is 1,795 pounds. Table 5-8 provides specifications and performance data on the Cessna Centurion. Table 5-9 gives the same data for the turbocharged model.

There is one other model of Centurion which is designed for a maximum in traveler comfort. It is the pressurized model shown in Fig. 5-8. The Pressurized Centurion provides 10,000 ft. cabin comfort at 20,000 feet. It has a 3.35 lb. pressure differential at the 20,000 feet altitude and will cruise at 230 mph for 811 statute miles.

List prices for the Centurion start at $76,250 for a standard equipped model and range upwards to about $90,000 with factory-installed avionics options. The Turbo Centurion starts at $84,100 and will cost upwards of $97,000 when equipped with avionics most often ordered for this plane. The Pressurized Centurion in

Fig. 5-7. Cessna Centurion (courtesy Cessna Aircraft Co.).

**Table 5-8. Performance Data And Specifications
For Cessna Centurion (courtesy Cessna Aircraft Co.).**

Wing Span: 36 ft. 9 in.
Wing Area: 175 ft.^{2}
Wing Loading: 21.7 lb/ft.^{2}
Length: 28 ft. 2 in.
Height: 9 ft. 8 in.
Engine: Teledyne Continental 10-520-L, 285 bhp @ 2700 rpm
Propeller: Constant speed, 3 blade, 80 in. dia.
Full Capacity: 90 gal.
Oil Capacity: 10 qt.
Empty Weight: 2133 lb.
Maximum Weight: 3800 lb.
Maximum Useful Load: 1679 lb.
Baggage Weight: 240 lb.
Speed, Max: 175 kts.
Speed, Cruise @ 75% Power: 171 kts.
Stall Speed
     Flaps Up: 65 kts.
     Flaps Down: 56 kts.
Rate Of Climb: 950 fpm
Service Ceiling: 17,300 ft.
Takeoff Distance
     Ground Roll: 1250 ft.
     Total Distance Over 50′ Obstacle: 2030 ft.
Landing Distance
     Ground Roll: 765 ft.
     Total Distance Over 50′ Obstacle: 1500 ft.

standard equipped form will cost $117,300 but can easily hit the $150,000 mark when equipped with avionics. Table 5-10 provides specifications and performance data for the Pressurized Centurion.

PIPER SARATOGA SP AND TURBO SARATOGA

The top of the line in the Piper single-engine category is the Saratoga SP and Turbo Saratoga SP. Shown in Fig. 5-9, both models offer 300 horsepower Lycoming engines and fuel tanks with 102 gallon capacities. The normally aspirated version has a range of 1,132 statute miles with a cruise speed of over 180 mph.

Passenger comfort is excellent due partially to the elimination of fatigue-inducing vibration by Piper's improved Dyna-Cushion engine mounts. These special vibration-absorbing mounts make even long trips less tiring.

The Turbo Saratoga SP is excellent for operating from high altitude airports and will maintain 75% power even at 20,000 feet. This model offers a top speed of 225 mph and the 300 horsepower engine gives a good short field capability.

The Saratoga SPs are six-passenger airplanes, but there is room to add a seventh seat if desired. Alternately, the owner can select deluxe conference seating with individual armrests, a thermal hot and cold refreshment center, and even a work table that stows neatly away.

Over each seat is an efficient fresh-air vent. A built-in oxygen system with overhead oxygen outlets can be specified for the turbocharged version. Double rear doors open to almost 4½ feet wide to allow the transporting of bulky cargo and to make entry and exit of passengers more convenient. In addition, fore and aft compartments provide almost 25 cubic feet of luggage space.

The Saratoga SP performance and specification data is provided in Table 5-11 and it sells for about $117,000 in the standard equipped version. Piper figures the average hourly operating expense to be slightly less than $50.00. The Turbo Saratoga SP lists for about $122,000 with an hourly operating expense of $54.63. Specifications and performance data for the turbocharged model are also shown in Table 5-11.

BEECHCRAFT BONANZA

The Beechcraft Bonanza is really a family of aircraft rather than a single airplane. Bonanzas have been popular topics of

Table 5-9. Performance Data and Specifications For Cessna Turbo Centurion (courtesy Cessna Aircraft Co.).

Wing Span: 36 ft. 9 in.
Wing Area: 175 ft.^{2}
Wing Loading: 22.9 lb/ft.^{2}
Length: 28 ft. 2 in.
Height: 9 ft. 8 in.
Engine: Teledyne Continental TS10-520-R, 285 bhp @ 2600
Propeller: Constant speed, 3 blade, 80 in. dia.
Fuel Capacity: 90 gal.
Oil Capacity: 11 qt.
Empty Weight: 2221 lb.
Maximum Weight: 4016 lb.
Maximum Useful Load: 1795 lb.
Baggage Weight: 240 lb.
Speed, Max: 204 kts.
Speed, Cruise @ 75% Power: 196 kts.
Stall Speed
    Flaps Up: 67 kts.
    Flaps Down: 58 kts.
Rate Of Climb: 930 fpm
Service Ceiling: 27,000 ft.
Takeoff Distance
    Ground Roll: 1300 ft.
    Total Distance Over 50' Obstacle: 2160 ft.
Landing Distance
    Ground Roll: 765 ft.
    Total Distance Over 50' Obstacle: 1500 ft.

conversation ever since they entered the market back in 1947. Fifteen hundred of the original model 35s were built, with the first forty having fabric-covered ailerons and flaps. After this, they were magnesium. Other changes included a redesigned cabin door, landing gear visual indicator lights, improved cabin ventilation and individual rear seat belts.

The Beechcraft Bonanza A35 was introduced in 1949 and was the first Bonanza to be certificated in the utility category. Additional changes emerged and Bonanzas began to have larger engines and fly faster. Gross weight was also increased, and in 1950, the airplane featured its first VHF radio transmitter. A third window was added to the fuselage of the Bonanza F35 in 1955.

The first Model 33 Bonanza, initially called the Debonair, made its appearance in 1960. It continued to be called the Debonair until 1968, when the E33 model was dubbed Bonanza. Joining the Bonanza family about the same time, the first Model 36 was certificated in the utility category in May 1968. It was designated A36 in 1969. The A36 became the leading Bonanza seller in 1975 and has remained so ever since.

The Beechcraft Bonanza 36 has been equipped ever since its introduction with a 285 horsepower Continental IO-520 engine, giving it the capacity to carry up to six passengers at speeds to 206 mph (179 knots). Its range is nearly 1,000 miles. The A36 models are readily identifiable by a fourth window in the fuselage. Their cabins are ten inches longer than the 33 and 35 series airplanes, and their double doors provide a spacious 45" × 40" cargo opening.

Club seating was offered for the first time in 1970, along with the convenience of an executive writing table. Air conditioning was made available as an option in 1975; and in 1977, the 1,000th Beechcraft Bonanza A36 was delivered. Recent improvements include an extended rear baggage compartment and optional 76 cubic foot oxygen supply. A 28-volt electrical system became standard in all Beechcraft Bonanza models in 1978.

A turbocharged model, named the Beechcraft Bonanza A36TC, (Fig. 5-10) was certificated in December 1978 and immediately proved highly popular. Powered by a 300 horsepower Continental engine, it has a 50 pound higher gross weight than the normally aspirated Bonanza A36 and utilizes a series of louvres and gills in the cowling to eliminate the need for cowl flaps. This model is certificated to 25,000 feet and can carry six people comfortable to their destinations at speeds up to 246 mph (213.75 knots). Propeller anti-icing is available on the A36TC and the airplane has

Fig. 5-8. Cessna Pressurized Centurion (courtesy Cessna Aircraft Co.).

**Table 5-10. Performance Data And Specifications For
Cessna Pressurized Centurion (courtesy Cessna Aircraft Co.).**

Wing Span: 36 ft. 9 in.
Wing Area: 175 ft.^{2}
Wing Loading: 22.9 lb .ft.^{2}
Length: 28 ft. 2 in.
Height: 9 ft. 8 in.
Engine: Teledyne Continental TS10-520-P, 285 bhp @ 2600 rpm
Propeller: Constant speed, 3 blade, 80 in. dia.
Fuel Capacity: 90 gal.
Oil Capacity: 11 qt.
Empty Weight: 2340 lb.
Maximum Weight: 4016 lb.
Maximum Useful Load: 1676 lb.
Baggage Weight: 200 lb.
Speed, Max: 206 kts.
Speed, Cruise @ 75% Power: 200 kts.
Stall Speed
    Flap Up: 67 kts.
    Flaps Down: 58 kts.
Rate Of Climb: 930 fpm
Service Ceiling: 23,000 ft.
Takeoff Distance
    Ground Roll: 1300 ft.
    Total Distance Over 50' Obstacle: 2160 ft.
Landing Distance
    Ground Roll: 765 ft.
    Total Distance Over 50' Obstacle: 1500 ft.

an improved heater that delivers up to 20% more BTUs than other Bonanza models.

Product improvements are being made continuously to the Beechcraft Bonanza line, but the airplanes still retain their quality heritage built into the first Bonanza introduced in 1947 by Walter Beech. Among the improvements for the new model Bonanzas, owners can expect to see new interiors on the Beechcraft Bonanza F33A and in the V35B models shown in Fig. 5-11. The headliner is a single piece for a cleaner appearance and is constructed of a sound-absorbing foam designed to reduce cabin sound levels. The sidewalls are recessed to provide an inch of additional elbow room over earlier models, and a host of new fabric, leather and vinyl inserts are available to allow customers to personalize their aircraft as never before.

The airspeed indicator is now graduated in knots only, resulting in a less cluttered instrument that is easier to read at a glance. The fuel flow gauge, previously graduated in a logarithmic scale, now has linear graduation. An electronic fuel flow sensor has replaced the mechanical sensor and contributes to substantially greater gauge accuracy. A starter-engaged annunciator light is installed to tell the pilot if the starter motor continues to run after the engine starts. It alerts him immediately and allows him to avert

Fig. 5-9. Piper Saratoga SP (courtesy Piper Aircraft Corp.).

Table 5-11. Performance Data And Specifications For Piper Saratoga SP and Turbo Saratoga (courtesy Piper Aircraft Corp.).

	SARATOGA SP	TURBO SARATOGA SP
Wing Span:	36.2 ft.	36.2 ft.
Wing Area:	178.3 ft.^{2}	178.3 ft.^{2}
Wing Loading:	20.2 lb/ft.^{2}	20.2 lb/ft.^{2}
Length:	27.7 ft.	28.3 ft.
Height:	8.5 ft.	8.5 ft.
Cabin Width:	49.0 in.	49.0 in.
Cabin Height:	49.0 in.	49.0 in.
Headroom		
Front:	36 in.	36 in.
Rear:	36 in.	36 in.
Engine: Lycoming 10-540-K1G5D, 300 bhp @ 2700		Lyc. T10-540-S1AD, 300 bhp @ 2700
Propeller: Hartzell constant speed, 2 blade, 80 in. dia		
Fuel Capcity:	102 gal.	102 gal.
Oil Capacity:	12 qt.	12 qt.
Empty Weight:	1994 lb.	2066 lb.
Maximum Weight:	3600 lb.	3600 lb.
Maximum Useful Load:	1621 lb.	1551 lb.
Baggage		
Weight:	100 lb.	100 lb.
Volume:	24.3 ft.^{3}	24.3 ft.^{3}
Speed, Max:	164 kts.	195 kts.
Speed, Cruise @ 75% Power:	159 kts.	177 kts.
Stall Speed		
Flaps Up:	60 kts.	61 kts.
Flaps Down:	57 kts.	56 kts.
Rate Of Climb:	1010 fpm	1120 fpm
Service Ceiling:	16,700 ft.	20,000 + ft.
Takeoff Distance		
Ground Roll:	1183 ft.	1110 ft.
Total Distance Over 50' Obstacle:	1795 ft.	1590 ft.
Landing Distance		
Ground Roll:	732 ft.	732 ft.
Total Distance Over 50' Obstacle:	1612 ft.	1725 ft.

a starter failure should such a condition occur. All the airplane's circuit breakers are now the push-pull type, permitting the pilot to isolate any electrical circuit, thus providing for a greater margin of safety.

Color-coded control knobs provide a visual reminder for the pilot that he has selected the correct control, in addition to the

Table 5-12. Performance Data and Specifications For Beechcraft Bonanza F33A (courtesy Beech Aircraft Corp.).

Wing Span: 33 ft. 6 in.	Volume: 35 ft.^{3}
Wing Area: 181 ft.^{2}	Speed, Max: 182 kts.
Wing Loading: 18.8 lbs/ft.^{2}	Speed, Cruise @ 75% Power: 172 kts.
Length: 26 ft. 8 in.	Stall Speed
Height: 8 ft. 3 in.	Flaps Up: 64 kts.
Cabin Width: 42 in.	Flaps Down: 51 kts.
Cabin Height: 50 in.	Rate Of Climb: 1167 fpm
Fuel Capacity: 74 gal.	Service Ceiling: 17,858 ft.
Oil Capacity: 12 qt.	Takeoff Distance
Empty Weight: 2125 lb.	Ground Roll: 1002 ft.
Maximum Weight: 3400 lb.	Total Distance Over 50' Obstacle: 1769 ft.
Maximum Useful Load: 1287 lb.	Landing Distance
Baggage	Ground Roll: 763 ft.
Weight: 270 lb.	Total Distance Over 50' Obstacle: 1324 ft.

current individualized shaping that provides tactile assurance. An optional overhead vent blower improves cabin ventilation in aircraft equipped both with and without air conditioning. An optional Aero Mechanism counter-drum altimeter is now available which will tell the pilot his altitude at a glance with no confusion, particularly at altitudes above 10,000 feet.

Standard equipped Beechcraft Bonanzas start at $91,950 for either the V35B or F33A model. The A36 starts at just under $100,000, with the turbocharged version starting at about $111,000. These are fly-away prices from the factory in Wichita, Kansas. Tables 5-12 through 5-15 provide performance data

Fig. 5-10. Beechcraft Bonanza A36 and A36TC (courtesy Beech Aircraft Corp.).

Fig. 5-11. Beechcraft Bonanza F33A and V35B (courtesy Beech Aircraft Corp.).

specifications for the F33A, V35B, A36 and A36TC (turbocharged), respectively.

SUMMARY

It can be seen from this discussion on single-engine, retractable gear aircraft that most of the planes are simply retractable gear versions of other fixed gear aircraft in each manufacturer's line. This is evidenced by the Cessna Skylane RG, the Piper Saratoga SP, and others. The planes originally came out as fixed gear models and after they became well established, the retractable gear designs were introduced. Both designs offer comparable seating room and transport capabilities, but "pulling up" the gear

Wing Span: 33 ft. 6 in.
Wing Area: 181 ft.^{2}
Wing Loading: 18.8 lbs/ft.^{2}
Length: 26 ft. 5 in.
Height: 7 ft. 7 in.
Cabin Width: 42 in.
Cabin Height: 50 in.
Fuel Capacity: 74 gal.
Oil Capacity: 12 qt.
Empty Weight: 2106 lb.
Maximum Weight: 3400 lb.
Maximum Useful Load: 1306 lb.
Baggage
    Weight: 270 lb.
    Volume: 35 ft.^{3}
Speed, Max: 182 kts.
Speed, Cruise @ 75% Power: 172 kts.
Stall Speed
    Flaps Up: 64 kts.
    Flaps Down: 51 kts.
Rate Of Climb: 1167 fpm
Service Ceiling: 17,858 ft.
Takeoff Distance
    Ground Roll: 1002 ft.
    Total Distance Over 50' Obstacle: 1769 ft.
Landing Distance
    Ground Roll: 763 ft.
    Total Distance Over 50' Obstacle: 1324 ft.

Table 5-13. Performance Data and Specifications For Beechcraft Bonanza V35B (courtesy Beech Aircraft Corp.).

provides a substantial savings in fuel and much improved speed characteristics.

Retractable gear aircraft cost considerably more than their fixed gear counterparts. For this reason, the potential aircraft

Table 5-14. Performance Data and Specifications For Beechcraft Bonanza A36 (courtesy Beech Aircraft Corp.).

Wing Span: 33 ft. 6 in.	Volume: 37 ft.^{3}
Wing Area: 181 ft.^{2}	Speed, Max: 179 kts.
Wing Loading: 19.9 lbs/ft.^{2}	Speed, Cruise @ 75%Power: 168 kts.
Length: 27 ft. 6 in.	Stall Speed
Height: 8 ft. 5 in.	Flaps Up: 62 kts.
Cabin Width: 42 in.	Flaps Down: 52 kts.
Cabin Height: 50 in.	Rate Of Climb: 1030 fpm
Fuel Capacity: 74 gal.	Service Ceiling: 16,600 ft.
Oil Capacity: 12 qt.	Takeoff Distance
Empty Weight: 2195 lb.	Ground Roll: 1140 ft.
Maximum Weight: 3600 lb.	Total Distance Over 50' Obstacle: 2040 ft.
Maximum Useful Load: 1417 lb.	Landing Distance
Baggage	Ground Roll: 840 ft.
Weight: 400 lb.	Total Distance Over 50' Obstacle: 1450 ft.

```
Wing Span: 33 ft. 6 in.
Wing Area: 181 ft.²
Wing Loading: 20.2 lbs/ft.²
Length: 27 ft. 6 in.
Height: 8 ft. 5 in.
Cabin Width: 42 in.
Cabin Height: 50 in.
Fuel Capacity: 74 gal.
Oil Capacity: 12 qt.
Empty Weight: 2278 lb.
Maximum Weight: 3650 lb.
Maximum Useful Load: 1388 lb.
Baggage
       Weight: 400 lb.
       Volume: 37 ft.³
Speed, Max: 214 kts.
Speed, Cruise @ 75% Power: 190 kts.
Stall Speed
       Flaps Up: 67 kts.
       Flaps Down: 57 kts.
Rate Of Climb: 1165 fpm
Service Ceiling: 25,000 + ft.
Takeoff Distance
       Ground Roll: 847 ft.
       Total Distance Over 50' Obstacle: 1758 ft.
Landing Distance
       Ground Roll: 721 ft.
       Total Distance Over 50' Obstacle: 1449 ft.
```

Table 5-15. Performance Data and Specifications For Beechcraft Bonanza A36TC (courtesy Beech Aircraft Corp.).

buyer must decide whether the speed and economy advantages outweigh the increased price for his or her particular needs. The least expensive aircraft in relation to list price may *not* be the least expensive over its entire operational life when compared to another type of aircraft more suitably designed for certain specific applications.

When speed, performance and handling abilities of an aircraft coupled with economical higher altitude operations are desirable, the retractable gear airplane of the single-engine variety is often the best choice. The capabilities of this type of aircraft will often more than offset the increased initial price and higher maintenance costs when compared to a similar aircraft of fixed gear design.

Chapter 6

Twin Engine Aircraft

In many ways, a *twin engine* aircraft is very different from those of single engine design. One must remember that in addition to the extra engine, the plane requires a control system which is much more complex. Even the engine gauges are multiplied. The airframe is designed to different specifications in order to withstand the higher stresses which are encountered with twin engine designs. Most often, the engines will be mounted midway along the wing sections; however, one plane discussed in this chapter is a tandem twin with one engine mounted at the nose in standard fashion and another mounted behind. In many ways, this particular plane handles and is designed along the lines of a single engine aircraft.

The pilot of a twin engine aircraft must have a more advanced license than those who fly only single engine designs. Flying these aircraft mandates skills which require additional hours of instruction in order to receive a twin engine rating.

All modern American twin engine aircraft have retractable landing gear and most of them incorporate variable-pitch constant-speed propellers for maximum efficiency. Safety is one major reason why many aircraft owners choose a twin engine aircraft. Performance capabilities are usually better, although some of the larger single engine craft may rival a twin in both performance and load capabilities while costing less. The safety feature is obvious. Should one engine fail, there is another which can provide a backup. It must be remembered, though, that twin engine airplanes are structurally designed to fly with *two* engines.

When one is out, the aircraft handles differently and special precautions must be taken. This is the reason for the special license requirement.

There are many criteria to consider when buying a twin engine aircraft. Unlike single engine design, which offers seating capacities of from one to seven or more persons, twin engine planes offer minimum seating of at least four persons. (The exception to this is the new two-place Wing Derringer.) An aircraft buyer who wants the dependability of a twin engine plane but only wishes seating capacity for two ends up with at least two wasted seats. If these latter two seats are never to be used or even the space they occupy used for transporting purposes, then much of the airplane (and the extra cost involved) is a useless expenditure. For this reason, twin engine aircraft are most often opted for by persons who desire a large seating or hauling capacity in *addition* to the better dependability and performance characteristics. Pilots who do not require the carrying volume discussed will most often stick to small single-engine aircraft which are designed to carry two persons. The capabilities, performance-wise, of the twin engine plane can be duplicated or even bettered by high performance, turbocharged singles. These, of course, still do not offer the dependability only an extra engine can provide.

BEECHCRAFT DUCHESS

The Beechcraft Duchess shown in Fig. 6-1 is a 171 knot (197 mph) twin powered by two Lycoming 4-cylinder engines rated at 180 horsepower each. On a more practical basis, it will cruise comfortably at 158 knots (182 mph) at 10,000 feet. Even economy cruise power settings provide 174 mph cruise with an effective range at 12,000 feet of 898 statute miles. This includes all but 45 minutes of reserve fuel. Two 50 gallon tanks provide enough fuel for a 717 statute mile cruise at a maximum power. In this configuration, the plane will provide a speed of 191 mph at 6,000 feet.

At a maximum weight of 3,900 pounds, the Beechcraft Duchess climbs out at 1,248 fpm at sea level on two engines. Single-engine rate of climb at sea level is 235 fpm.

Landing gear for this plane is the same proven Beechcraft design which is used on nearly all of their planes. This arrangement features retractable tricycle gear with a steerable, self-centering nose wheel. Hydraulic brakes with toe-operated controls on the rudder pedals is a standard feature. As far as the cabin is

Fig. 6-1. Beechcraft Duchess (courtesy Beech Aircraft Corp.).

113

Wing Span: 38 ft.
Wing Area: 181 ft.^{2}
Wing Loading: 21.5 lb/ft.^{2}
Length: 29 ft. ½ in.
Height: 9 ft. 6 in.
Cabin Width: 44 in.
Cabin Height: 48 in.
Headroom
    Front: 37.5 in.
    Rear: 35.5 in.
Fuel Capacity: 100 gal.
Oil Capacity: 8 qts/eng.
Empty Weight: 2460 lb.
Maximum Weight: 3900 lb.
Maximum Useful Load: 1456 lb.
Baggage
    Weight: 200 lb.
    Volume: 19.5 ft.^{3}
Speed, Max: 171 kts.
Speed, Cruise @ 75% Power: 158 kts.
Stall Speed
    Flaps Up: 70 kts.
    Flaps Down: 60 kts.
Rate Of Climb: 1248 fpm; single 235 fpm
Service Ceilings: 19650 ft.; single 6170 ft.
Takeoff Distance
    Ground Roll: 1017 ft.
    Total Distance Over 50' Obstacle: 2119 ft.
Landing Distance
    Ground Roll: 1000 ft.
    Total Distance Over 50' Obstacle: 1881 ft.

Table 6-1. Performance Data and Specifications For Beechcraft Duchess (courtesy Beech Aircraft Corp.).

concerned, the Beechcraft Duchess provides left and right entrance doors with a baggage door on the left side only. Inside, there are adjustable seats with three-position reclining seat backs. A two-place rear bench seat is also provided and may be placed in the cargo hold to carry two additional passengers. Total capacity of this rear area is only 200 pounds, so only small passengers such as children may be seated here.

Standard engine instruments include dual manifold pressure gauge, two recording tachometers, loadmeters, fuel gauges, oil pressure and temperature gauges, fuel pressure gauges, and cylinder head temperature gauges.

The Beechcraft Duchess is a small twin which can easily be operated from short runways. Landing distance at maximum weight is 1,881 feet over a 50 foot obstacle.

Table 6-1 provides performance data and specifications for the Beechcraft Duchess which offers an alternate static air source, emergency locator transmitter and central door latches as standard equipment. The two counter-rotating Lycoming 4-cylinder normally aspirated engines combined with the airframe structure provide a relatively fast aircraft with a useful load of nearly 1,500 pounds. Standard base price is $107,000.

CESSNA MODEL 310

The Cessna Aircraft Company in Wichita, Kansas celebrated the silver anniversary of the Cessna Model 310 in 1980, marking 25 years of versatility and reliability that has characterized more than 5,100 310s that have been delivered since the airplane's inception in 1955. The 310's appearance has changed during the airplane's quarter-century of production, with major alterations including a swept tail in 1960, a rear window in 1972 and an extended nose in 1975. The airplane's sleek, distinctive lines contribute significantly to its continuing popularity in the marketplace.

Inside the new version of the 310, the pilot will appreciate the relocation of the Radio Magnetic Indicator (RMI), Distance Measuring Equipment (DME), and number two Nav Indicator one position clockwise to position the RMI next to the Horizontal Situation Indicator (HSI) for a quicker, more efficient scan.

Optional improvements include new 100 amp alternators which offer long-life power with less weight than previous 100 amp units. An optional cabin stereo system is also available, with pneumatic headphones and improved jacks for enhanced airborne listening and two overhead speakers for ground stereo operation.

The 310's performance remains a key factor in its continuing appeal to customers. With a new change in the pilot's operating handbook format, the entire Cessna line now reflects information that is consistent with a FAR Part 91.22 requirement for VFR fuel reserves. Rather than showing a 45 minute reserve at 45% power, reserves are now based on the particular cruise power selected. For example, if you cruise at 75% power, the 45 minute reserve is also calculated at 75% power. The 310 range is 1,078 nautical (1,241 statute) miles with full fuel of 1,218 pounds and a cruise speed of 193 knots (222 mph) at 7,500 feet. The Turbo 310 will cruise 1,197 nautical (1,378 statute) miles at 20,000 feet and 73.6% power at 221 knots (254 mph) on 1,218 pounds of fuel.

New exterior styling includes a durable polyurethane finish in a variety of colors. Inside, armrests, seats and seatbacks feature vinyl inserts that are color coordinated to seat fabrics. An optional vinyl beverage caddy with two stainless steel beverage containers is also available to 310 buyers.

Figure 6-2 shows the Cessna 310, which starts at $137,600 for the normally aspirated model. The Turbo 310 lists at $160,650. Both prices are for standard equipped airplanes. The 310 has six-seat capability and room for a lot of instruments, including weather radar. Figure 6-3 shows the seat arrangement along with a full instrument panel. The Cessna II package offers many avionics and accessories as standard equipment and boosts the price of each basic model by about $28,000. Table 6-2 provides performance data and specifications for the normally aspirated 310, while Table 6-3 provides the same data for the turbocharged T310.

PIPER SENECA II

The Piper Seneca II shown in Fig. 6-4 is a six-place turbocharged twin which exhibits a full 200 horsepower in each engine even when climbing through 14,000 feet. If you need to fly even higher, the power is there to fly well over heavy traffic and find the tailwinds that can increase speed and keep fuel consumption down. With a service ceiling for 25,000 feet, the Piper Seneca II can fly well above many bad weather conditions. This can mean a fuel savings in itself by flying over weather conditions rather than around them. An optional built-in oxygen system makes even high altitude trips more convenient.

The Seneca II offers excellent short field capabilities, clearing a 50 foot obstacle in just 1,240 feet. This means that owners of this plane are not limited to major airports that may still be a long distance from a final destination. This aircraft is designed to handle rough field touchdowns. The heavy-duty oleo struts take the blows unpaved fields can deliver. Additionally, the wide track wheel base adds stability even in unexpected crosswinds.

As is indicated by its picture, the Seneca II is a rather stocky airplane. Its fuselage does not taper as much as some other models, so cabin room is rather spacious for a twin in this category. Wide contoured seats in many different fabrics and color schemes can be chosen. The all-front-facing seating arrangement will allow for an optional seventh seat. Face-to-face conference style seating offers a hot and cold refreshment locker and wood-grained work table. Each seat has an overhead seating light and fresh air vent. Individual oxygen outlets and air conditioning can be ordered as options. Forward and rear doors eliminate the need to climb over forward seats when entering and exiting.

As a utility aircraft, the Seneca II is quickly converted. Passenger seats can be removed to allow for more interior cargo

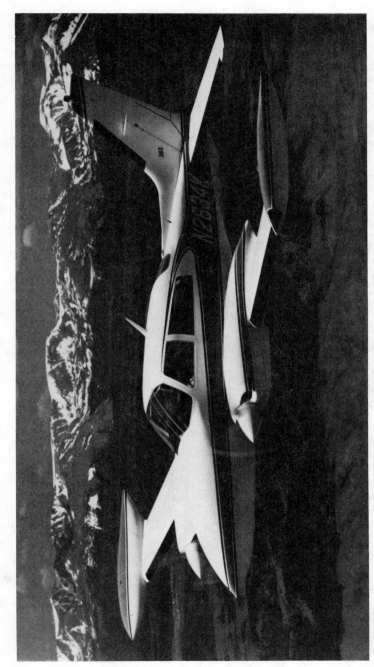

Fig. 6-2. Cessna 310 (courtesy Cessna Aircraft Co.).

Fig. 6-3. Cessna 310 instrument panel and seating arrangement (courtesy Cessna Aircraft Co.).

space than many comparable twins. Fore and aft compartments combine for over 32 cubic feet of baggage space.

The Seneca II provides excellent performance figures at a consumption of about 18 gallons per hour, which is very good for a twin engine plane. Maximum speed is 196 knots (225 mph) with a 75% cruise speed of about 218 mph. It has a range of over 1,000 miles at 55% power with a 45 minute reserve. At a maximum gross weight of 4,570 pounds, the useful load of this turbocharged twin is 1,731 pounds.

Table 6-4 provides performance data and specifications for this aircraft, which is base priced at $177,955. Piper estimates the total operating expense per hour for the Seneca II to be $76.51. This is based on an average fuel consumption of 22.1 gph at $1.75 per gallon.

PIPER AZTEC F

The Piper Aztec shown in Fig. 6-5 has been around for a long time. In recent years, its nose has been elongated and brought out to an aerodynamic point. Earlier models had stubbier noses, but generally, the abilities of the new Aztec F are the same as for its predecessors. These abilities mainly involve all-around operation in rough weather from rough airstrips and with oversized loads, be they cargo or passengers. Of course, the new Aztec F has many built-in refinements, modifications and improvements over the earlier models. But all of these have not decreased its ability to be flown in all sorts of operations. Too often, certain aircraft improvements will have deleterious effects on other aspects of its flight performance. An increase in horsepower may result in a faster takeoff at the expense of decreased range or hauling ability. An increase in speed through aerodynamic changes to the fuselage may decrease certain short field capabilities. Fortunately for the aircraft buyer who is looking for a rugged all-around airplane, the Aztec is still the workhorse of the light twin engine line.

Table 6-2. Performance Data and Specifications
For Cessna Model 310 (courtesy Cessna Aircraft Co.).

Wing Span: 36 ft. 11 in.
Wing Area: 179 ft.^{2}
Wing Loading: 30.73 lb/ft.^{2}
Length: 31 ft. 11½ in.
Height: 10 ft. 8 in.
Engine: (2) Teledyne Continental 10-520-MB, 285 bhp each.
Propeller: Constant speed, full feathering, 3 blades, 76.5 in. dia.
Fuel Capacity: 102 gal. (up to 207 gal.)
Oil Capacity: 26 qt.
Empty Weight: 3352 lb.
Maximum Weight: 5500 lb.
Maximum Useful Load: 2183 lb.
Baggage Weight: 950 lb.
Speed, Max: 207 kts.
Speed, Cruise @ 75% Power: 195 kts.
Stall Speed
       Flaps Up: 78 kts.
       Flaps Down: 70 kts.
Rate Of Climb: 1662; 370 single
Service Ceiling: 19,750; 7400 single
Takeoff Distance
       Ground Roll: 1335 ft.
       Total Distance Over 50' Obstacle: 1700 ft.
Landing Distance
       Ground Roll: 640 ft.
       Total Distance Over 50' Obstacle: 1790 ft.

**Table 6-3. Performance Data and Specifications
For Cessna Turbo Model 310 (courtesy Cessna Aircraft Co.).**

Wing Span: 36 ft. 11 in.
Wing Area: 179 ft.^{2}
Wing Loading: 30.73 lb/ft.^{2}
Length: 31 ft. 11 in.
Height: 10 ft. 8 in.
Engine: (2) Teledyne Continental turbocharged TS10-520-BB, 285 bhp each.
Propeller: Constant speed, full feathering, 3 blades, 78 in. dia.
Fuel Capacity: 102 gal. (up to 207 gal.)
Oil Capacity: 26 qt.
Empty Weight: 3473 lb.
Maximum Weight: 5500 lb.
Maximum Useful Load: 2062 lb.
Baggage Weight: 950 lb.
Speed, Max: 237 kts.
Speed, Cruise @ 75% Power: 201 kts.
Stall Speed
    Flaps Up: 78 kts.
    Flaps Down: 70 kts.
Rate Of Climb: 1700 fpm; 390 fpm single
Service Ceiling: 27,400 ft.; 17,200 ft. single
Takeoff Distance
    Ground Roll: 1306 ft.
    Total Distance Over 50' Obstacle: 1662 ft.
Landing Distance
    Ground Roll: 640 ft.
    Total Distance Over 50' Obstacle: 1790 ft.

The Aztec F is quite comfortable on dirt fields. The heavy-duty nose wheel strut is set back, in line with the propellers, in order to give them better ground clearance when taxiing over bumps. You can also take the Aztec F in and out of airstrips that are too short for other aircraft. It takes off and lands in under 1,000 feet at sea level and can be flown at an airspeed as low as 70 knots without stalling. In the Aztec, Piper has reached an excellent liaison between economical high speed performance and the ability, when needed, to fly low and slow. Many planes are capable of performing each of these requirements, but few can accomplish both.

The normally aspirated Aztec F utilizes 250 horsepower Lycoming engines which combine with the aerodynamics of the Aztec to develop a cruising speed of 179 knots (206 mph). They will provide many air miles of service with their 2,000 hour TBO.

Range of the normally aspirated Aztec is 1,134 statute miles in standard configuration. Owners can order tip tanks that are built right into the wing and increase the range to over 1,500 statute miles. This means that the Aztec F with tip tanks could typically fly

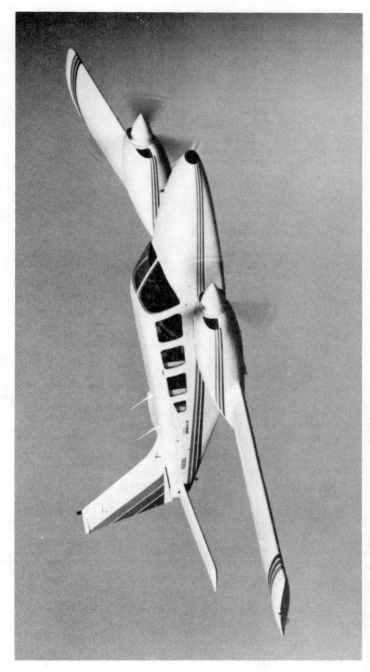

Fig. 6-4. Piper Seneca II (courtesy Piper Aircraft Corp.).

**Table 6-4. Performance Data and Specifications
For Piper Seneca II (courtesy Piper Aircraft Corp.).**

Wing Span: 38.9 ft.
Wing Area: 208.7 ft.^{2}
Wing Loading: 21.9 lb/ft.^{2}
Length: 28.6 ft.
Height: 9.9 ft.
Cabin Width: 49 in.
Cabin Height: 49 in.
Headroom
    Front: 36 in.   Middle: 36 in.
    Rear: 35 in.
Engine: (2) Continental TS10-360-E, 200 bhp @ 2575 rpm each
Propeller: Hartzell constant speed, full feathering, 76 in. dia.
Fuel Capacity: 93 gal. (up to 123 gal.)
Oil Capacity: 8 qt. (each)
Empty Weight: 2839 lb.
Maximum Weight: 4570 lb.
Maximum Useful Load: 1731 lb.
Baggage
    Weight: 200 lb.
    Volume: 32.6 ft.^{3}
Speed, Max: 196 kts.
Speed, Cruise @ 75% Power: 190 kts.
Stall Speed
    Flaps Up: 63 kts.
    Flaps Down: 61 kts.
Rate Of Climb: 1340 fpm; 225 fpm single
Service Ceiling: 25,000 + ft.; 13,400 ft. single
Takeoff Distance
    Ground Roll: 870 ft.
    Total Distance Over 50' Obstacle: 1240 ft.
Landing Distance
    Ground roll: 1380 ft.
    Total Distance Over 50' Obstacle: 2110 ft.

from Colorado Springs, Colorado to Silver Spring, Maryland, non-stop, and still have a 45 minute fuel reserve.

As is the case with many twins today, owners who need an extra degree of performance may order the turbocharged version. The Turbo Aztec F flies faster than its normally aspirated cousin at 242 mph and has a service ceiling of 24,000 feet. At this altitude, the Turbo Aztec F still has 75% power available. The turbocharged engine has an 1,800 hour TBO.

As a passenger plane, the Aztec has many convenience features, such as reading lights, ashtrays, and armrests. Alternately, you can turn the extra-wide passenger cabin into a large cargo hold by removing the rear seats, center seats, and rear bulkhead. There is ample room to keep normal baggage out of the way in nose and aft compartments which will hold a total of 300 pounds.

Table 6-5 provides performance data and specifications for the Aztec F and Turbo Aztec F. The standard version of the Aztec F

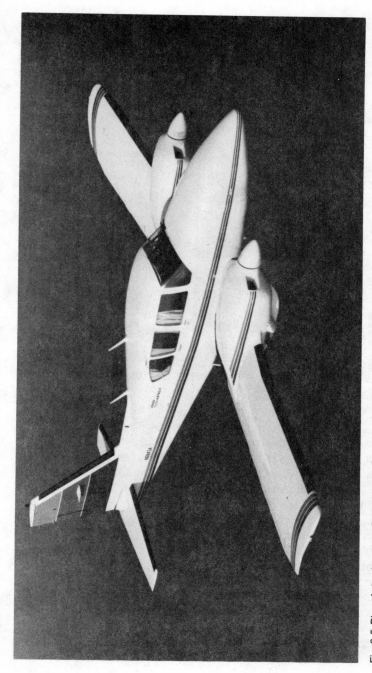

Fig. 6-5. Piper Aztec (courtesy Piper Aircraft Corp.).

123

AZTEC F	TURBO AZTEC F
Wing Span: 37.3 ft.	37.3 ft.
Wing Area: 207 ft.2	207 ft.2
Wing Loading: 25.1 lb/ft.2	25.1 lb/ft.2
Length: 31.2 ft.	31.2 ft.
Height: 10.1 ft.	10.1 ft.
Cabin Width: 45 in.	45 in.
Cabin Height: 50.5 in.	50.5 in.
Fuel Capacity: 137 gal. (up to 177 gal.)	137 gal. (up to 177 gal.)
Oil Capacity: 12 qt. each	12 qt. each
Empty Weight: 3184 lb.	3323 lb.
Maximum Weight: 5200 lb.	5200 lb.
Maximum Useful Load: 2016 lb.	1877 lb.
Baggage	
Weight: 300 lb.	300 lb.
Volume: 40.4 ft.3	40.4 ft.3
Speed, Max: 179 kts.	215 kts.
Speed, Cruise @ 75% Power: 170 kts.	193 kts.
Stall Speed	
Flaps Up: 61.0 kts.	61.0 kts.
Flaps Down: 54.5 kts.	54.5 kts.
Rate of Climb: 1400 fpm; 235 fpm single	1470 fpm; 225 fpm single
Service Ceiling: 17,600 ft.; 4800 ft. single	24,000 ft.; 13,300 ft. single
Takeoff Distance	
Ground Roll: 1190 ft.	1015 ft.
Total Distance Over 50' Obstacle: 1980 ft.	1695 ft.
Landing Distance	
Ground Roll: 950 ft.	950 ft.
Total Distance Over 50' Obstacle: 1585 ft.	1585 ft.

lists for $215,470. Piper estimates the total hourly operating expense at just under $80.00.

CESSNA 335

Cessna advertises the 335 as the lowest-priced, cabin-class business twin on the market. Shown in Fig. 6-6, it is powered by two 300 horsepower turbocharged engines, each rated at 1,400 hours TBO. It will cruise at 195 knots (224 mph) at 74% power and 10,000 feet. Maximum range with full fuel of 1,218 pounds is 945 nautical (1,088 statute) miles, also at 10,000 feet.

With the comfort and convenience of a six-place airborne conference room, optional refreshment center and/or writing table, the 335 makes an excellent business transport for companies that desire the performance and safety advantages of a twin without the need for cabin pressurization. In addition to the refreshment center and writing table, individual air vents, reading lights, air conditioning and stereo are also available as options. The air conditioning system is equipped with a separate circuit breaker for each evaporator blower assembly and can be operated at 50% capacity should one blower be inoperative. The stereo system

Fig. 6-6. Cessna 335 (courtesy Cessna Aircraft Co.).

125

includes pneumatic headphones and two overhead speakers for airborne or ground listening.

With a twin engine service ceiling of 26,800 feet, the 335 is quite capable of climbing above many weather conditions. Twin engine rate of climb at sea level is 1,400 fpm. Fly-away prices at the factory for the Model 335 start at $209,950. With optional instrumentation package installed at the factory, the price climbs an additional $26,000. Figure 6-7 shows the conference seating arrangement from the aft position forward. Table 6-6 provides performance data and specifications.

BEECHCRAFT BARON

1981 marked the 20th year of production of the Beechcraft Baron line of high performance business aircraft (Fig. 6-8). In that time, approximately 5,300 Barons have been sold throughout the world, amounting to some $552 million in retail sales. The basic Beechcraft Baron Model 55 was introduced in November 1960 as an outgrowth of the Beechcraft Travel Air. The horsepower rating of the Baron was increased to 260 hp versus the 180 hp rating of the Travel Air. Improvements included all-weather capability and airframe refinements including a swept vertical tail, flat deck nacelles and full action Fowler flaps for short field operations. The Model 55 had a gross weight of 4,880 pounds (2,214 kg), a useful load of 1,920 pounds (871 kg) and a top speed of 230 mph (200 knots). It had four-place seating with an optional fifth seat.

Slight changes were made in the A-Model which debuted in 1962. The B55 followed the next year with an increase in gross weight to 5,000 pounds, a longer nose cone which provided a 12 cubic foot nose baggage compartment and an optional 142 gallon fuel supply. By the end of the third sales year, a total of 500 Beechcraft Barons had been produced.

In 1965, the Beechcraft Baron C55 was introduced. Powered by two Continental six-cylinder IO-520-C, 285 hp engines, the C55 had a gross weight of 5,300 pounds, a useful load of 2,285 pounds and a top speed of 242 mph (210 knots). The C55 offered a standard baggage compartment and a one-piece windshield. During 1965, Beech delivered its 1,000th Baron 55 and in 1966, a C55 flew around the world in five days, six hours and 16 minutes to demonstrate its reliability.

In May 1967, Beech introduced the turbocharged Baron 56TC. The new turbo Baron was designed to cruise 290 mph (252 knots) at 25,000 feet and would climb in excess of 2,000 fpm.

Service ceiling was 34,500 feet. The 56TC was powered by Lycoming TIO-541, fuel-injected 380 hp engines, which were eventually used in the Beechcraft Duke. This was the first Beechcraft Baron to offer air conditioning. It had a useful load of 2,365 pounds and gross weight of 5,990 pounds. A total of 94 turbo Barons were produced between 1967 and 1971.

The first light twin to offer club seating was introduced by Beech Aircraft in 1969. It was the Beechcraft Baron Model 58, and it differed from other Baron models by having the upper forward fuselage extended by 10 inches and incorporating double passenger/cargo doors on the right side of the fuselage for easy entrance. The Model 58 also featured a fourth window on each side of the fuselage. An increase in single engine rate of climb was accomplished by extending the propeller shaft and redesigning the front of the engine cowl.

By December 1971, the Beechcraft Baron 58 had become the most popular Baron in the product lineup, commanding 58% of all Baron sales during that fiscal year. The pressurized Beechcraft Baron 58P was first delivered in 1976 as a logical evolution in providing fast, comfortable, economical transportation. Although similar to the unpressurized version in basic configuration, the

Fig. 6-7. Cessna 335 conference seating configuration (courtesy Cessna Aircraft Co.).

**Table 6-6. Performance Data and Specifications
For Cessna Model 335 (courtesy Cessna Aircraft Co.).**

Wing Span: 38 ft. 1.3 in.
Wing Area: 184 ft.^{2}
Wing Loading: 32.55 lb/ft.^{2}
Length: 34 ft. 4 in.
Height: 12 ft. 7 in.
Engine: (2) Teledyne Continental TS10-520-EB, 300 bhp (each)
Propeller: Constant speed, full feathering, 3 blades, 76.5 in. dia.
Fuel Capacity: 102 gal. (up to 166 gal.)
Oil Capacity: 26 qt.
Empty Weight: 3749 lb.
Maximum Weight: 5990 lb.
Maximum Useful Load: 2276 lb.
Baggage Weight: 930 lb.
Speed, Max: 230 lbs.
Speed, Cruise @ 175% Power: 215 kts.
Stall Speed
    Flaps Up: 79 kts.
    Flaps Down: 71 kts.
Rate Of Climb: 1400 fpm; 200 fpm single
Service Ceiling: 26,800 ft.; 11,500 ft. single
Takeoff Distance
    Ground Roll: 1850 ft.
    Total Distance Over 50′ Obstacle: 2365 ft.
Landing Distance
    Ground Roll: 770 ft.
    Total Distance Over 50′ Obstacle: 1850 ft.

Model 58P was designed, tested and type certificated under the latest and most stringent FAR, Part 23.

The original pressurized Baron featured two 310 hp Continental engines which offered a maximum cruise speed of 266 mph (231 knots) at 25,000 feet. The 58P offered automatic waste gates to allow the turbochargers to adjust without manual assist to altitude changes during climb and descent. Other features were automatic cabin altitude programmer, air conditioning, 300 pound nose baggage capacity, three-bladed propellers and dual streamlined oscillating beacons.

Also in 1976, Beech introduced the turbocharged version of the Model 58, the 58TC. The Model 58TC incorporated the engines, wings and landing gear of the 58P and like the 58P, it was certified under FAR, Part 23. In 1979, both the 58P and 58TC received the Continental TSIO-520-WB engines, boosting the horsepower from 310 to 325 and affording both aircraft a top speed of 300 mph (261 knots). At this time, both aircraft received a 100 pound gross weight/useful load increase. The 1980 and 1981

Fig. 6-8. Beechcraft Baron E55 (foreground) and Baron B55 (courtesy Beech Aircraft Corp.).

Wing Span: 37 ft. 10 in.
Wing Area: 199.2 ft.^{2}
Wing Loading: 25.6 lb/ft.^{2}
Length: 28 ft.
Height: 9 ft. 7 in.
Cabin Width: 42 in.
Cabin Height: 50 in.
Fuel Capacity: 100 gal. (136 gal. optional)
Oil Capacity: 12 qt. each
Empty Weight: 3236 lb.
Maximum Weight: 5100 lb.
Maximum Useful Load: 1855 lb.
Baggage
    Weight: 700 lb.
    Volume: 47 ft.^{3}
Speed, Max: 201 kts.
Speed, Cruise @ 75% Power: 188 kts.
Stall Speed
    Flaps Up: 79 kts.
    Flaps Down: 73 kts.
Rate Of Climb: 1693 fpm; 397 fpm single
Service Ceiling: 19,300 ft.; 6,400 ft. single
Takeoff Distance
    Ground Roll: 1400 ft.
    Total Distance Over 50' Obstacle: 2154 ft.
Landing Distance
    Ground Roll: 1467 ft.
    Total Distance Over 50' Obstacle: 2148 ft.

Table 6-7. Performance Data and Specifications For Beechcraft Baron B55 (courtesy Beech Aircraft Corp.).

Beechcraft Baron 58P and 58TC have a gross weight of 6,240 pounds and both airplanes boast a quiet, comfortable 277 mph (241 knots) maximum cruise speed.

The Beechcraft Baron family of five today offers customers a wide range of performance and load carrying configurations to meet each individual need. Figure 6-8 shows the 55 series, which includes the B55, with a base price of $141,500. It is powered by two Continental six-cylinder fuel-injected engines rated at 260 hp each. It has a maximum speed of 201 knots (231 mph) and a useful load of 1,885 pounds. The second plane in this series is the Baron E55 which is powered by two Continental six-cylinder engines, fuel-injected and rated at 285 mph each. This model has a useful load of over 2,000 pounds and a top speed of 239 mph. Standard list price at the factory is $173,750.

Both models in this series look very much the same, as they are basically the same airplane with different types of engines. Table 6-7 provides performance data and specifications for the B55, while Table 6-8 provides the same data for the E55.

The Baron 58 series is an elongated version of the 55 series just discussed. All three planes in this category, the 58, 58TC, and 58P, appear to be nearly identical at a casual glance. This basic design is shown in Fig. 6-9.

The first plane in this series is the standard Baron 58 which is powered by two Continental six-cylinder eingines rated at 285 hp each. These are the same engines used in the E55 series, so performance specifications are very close to those of the E55. The 58 offers increased range over the former airplane by carrying 194 gallons of usable fuel. This is some 25 gallons more than with the E55. Table 6-9 provides a complete chart of information for the Baron 58.

The Baron 58TC is a turbocharged aircraft powered by two Continental six-cylinder engines rated at 325 hp each. It has a maximum speed of 300 mph and can cruise at 277 mph at 25,000 feet, its service ceiling. In addition to its excellent performance, it is a plane capable of carrying a 2,447 pound useful load. Rate of climb at sea level is nearly 1,500 fpm with both engines and 270 fpm with only one. Maximum range with 190 gallons of usable fuel on

**Table 6-8. Performance Data And Specifications
For Beechcraft Baron E55 (courtesy Beech Aircraft Corp.).**

```
Wing Span: 37 ft. 10 in.
Wing Area: 199.2 ft.2
Wing Loading: 26.6 lb/ft.2
Length: 29 ft.
Height: 9 ft. 2 in.
Cabin Width: 42 in.
Cabin Height: 50 in.
Fuel Capacity: 100 gal. (166 gal. optional)
Oil Capacity: 12 qt. each
Empty Weight: 3269 lb.
Maximum Weight: 5300 lb.
Maximum Useful Load: 2055 lb.
Baggage
        Weight: 700 lb.
        Volume: 53 ft.3
Speed, Max: 208 kts.
Speed, Cruise @ 75% Power: 200 kts.
Stall Speed
        Flaps Up: 83 kts.
        Flaps Down: 73 kts.
Rate Of Climb: 1682 fpm; 388 fpm single
Service Ceiling: 19,100 ft.; 6600 ft. single
Takeoff Distance
        Ground Roll: 13.5 ft.
        Total Distance Over 50' Obstacle: 2050 ft.
Landing Distance
        Ground Roll: 1237 ft.
        Total Distance Over 50' Obstacle: 2202 ft.
```

Fig. 6-9. Beechcraft Baron 58 series basic design (courtesy Beech Aircraft Corp.).

board is 1,414 statute miles flying at 25,000 feet at 53% power. Table 6-10 gives the manufacturer's performance data and specifications.

The last in the Baron series is the 58P which is a pressurized version and very similar to the 58TC in both performance and specifications. Top speed, again, is 300 mph, with both planes using the same engines and having identical maximum takeoff weights. Useful load for the pressurized version is some 200 pounds less than for the non-pressurized TC, but cruise speeds are basically identical as is cruising range.

Both the 58P and 58TC were given a new propeller synchrophaser system as standard equipment in 1981. This is a replacement feature which, instead of just matching the propeller RPM of both engines, refines engine operation by electronically positioning engine firing orders at a preset optimum phase relationship. This results in less vibration and a more comfortable cabin environment. There is no restriction on the system, so it can be used during takeoff, landings, and all single-engine operations. Table 6-11 provides performance data and specifications for the

Table 6-9. Performance Data and Specifications For Beechcraft Baron 58 (courtesy Beech Aircraft Corp.).

Wing Span: 37 ft. 10 in.
Wing Area: 199.2 ft.^{2}
Wing Loading: 27.1 lb/ft.^{2}
Length: 29 ft. 10 in.
Height: 9 ft. 6 in.
Cabin Width: 42 in.
Cabin Height: 50 in.
Fuel Capacity: 136 gal. (194 gal. optional)
Oil Capacity: 12 qt. each
Empty Weight: 3361 lb.
Maximum Weight: 5400 lb.
Maximum Useful Load: 2063 lb.
Baggage
    Weight: 1020 lb.
    Volume: 77 ft.^{3}
Speed, Max: 208 kts.
Speed, Cruise @ 75% Power: 200 kts.
Stall Speed
    Flaps Up: 84 kts.
    Flaps Down: 74 kts.
Rate Of Climb: 1660 fpm; 390 fpm single
Service Ceiling: 18,600 ft.; 7000 ft. single
Takeoff Distance
    Ground Roll: 1336 ft.
    Total Distance Over 50' Obstacle: 2101 ft.
Landing Distance
    Ground Roll: 1439 ft.
    Total Distance Over 50' Obstacle: 2498 ft.

Wing Span: 37 ft. 10 in.
Wing Area: 188.1 ft.^{2}
Wing Loading: 33 lb/ft.^{2}
Length: 29 ft. 11 in.
Height: 9 ft. 2 in.
Cabin Width: 42 in.
Cabin Height: 50 in.
Fuel Capacity: 166 gal. (190 gal. optional)
Oil Capacity: 12 qt. each
Empty Weight: 3793 lb.
Maximum Weight: 6200 lb.
Maximum Useful Load: 2447 lb.
Baggage
    Weight: 1370 lb.
    Volume: 77 ft.^{3}
Speed, Max: 261 kts.
Speed, Cruise @ 75% Power: 241 kts.
Stall Speed
    Flaps Up: 84 kts.
    Flaps Down: 78 kts.
Rate Of Climb: 1475 fpm; 270 fpm single
Service Ceiling: 25000 + ft.; 13,490 ft. single
Takeoff Distance
    Ground Roll: 1555 ft.
    Total Distance Over 50' Obstacle: 2643 ft.
Landing Distance
    Ground Roll: 1378 ft.
    Total Distance Over 50' Obstacle: 2427 ft.

Table 6-10. Performance Data and Specifications For Beechcraft Baron 58TC (courtesy Beech Aircraft Corp.).

pressurized Baron 58P. Pricing of the 58 series starts at $201,750 for the Baron 58. If you want the turbocharged version, add another $26,000. The Baron 58P tops this series with a price of $271,500.

CESSNA SKYMASTER SERIES

The Cessna Skymaster shown in Fig. 6-10 uses tandem mounted engines, probably making it the safest of all twins to fly in an engine-out condition. The pusher engine is mounted at the back of the cabin and eliminates the normal aft fuselage section. This has been replaced with lightweight tail booms. This does have one disadvantage in that some useful storage space is eliminated by the boom section. With the engine configuration shown, this aircraft is powered by *centerline thrust*. This principle does not change even when one engine is shut down. The thrust is still through the centerline of the aircraft. This is not true of standard twins with wing-mounted engines where an engine shutdown results in asymmetrical thrust forces and difficulty for the pilot.

The Skymaster is available in three models. The standard Skymaster, Turbo Skymaster and Pressurized Skymaster are excellent airplanes for pilots who are transitioning to multi-engine operation. They combine the benefits of multi-engine reliability and high wing design with the best single-engine flight characteristics of any modern twin. The Skymaster also has extremely good short field takeoff and landing capabilities and is able to operate from many airports which would not tolerate other types of twins. The Skymaster has a cruise speed of 159 knots (195 mph) and a useful load of 1,861 pounds. Range, with 888 pounds of useful fuel at 75% power and a cruise altitude of 5,500 feet, is 1,082 statute miles.

The Turbo Skymaster has all of the features of the normally aspirated Skymaster plus the added advantages of sea level manifold pressure up to 17,000 feet. It will cruise at 200 knots (230 mph) at 80% power and at 20,000 feet. Range at that altitude and power setting is 1,065 statute miles with 888 pounds of usable fuel. Single-engine rate of climb is a respectable 335 fpm and maximum certificated operating altitude is 20,000 feet.

The Pressurized Skymaster provides a 10,000 foot cabin at 20,000 feet. It cruises at 205 knots (236 mph) at 75% power and

Table 6-11. Performance Data and Specifications For Beechcraft Baron 58P (courtesy Beech Aircraft Corp.).

Wing Span: 37 ft. 10 in.
Wing Area: 188.1 ft.^{2}
Wing Loading: 33 lb/ft.^{2}
Length: 29 ft. 11 in.
Height: 9 ft. 2 in.
Cabin Width: 42 in.
Cabin Height: 50 in.
Fuel Capacity: 166 gal. (190 gal. optional)
Oil Capacity: 12 qt. each
Empty Weight: 4018 lb.
Maximum Weight: 6200 lb.
Maximum Useful Load: 2222 lb.
Baggage
    Weight: 1020 lb.
    Volume: 77 ft.^{3}
Speed, Max: 261 kts.
Speed, Cruise @ 75% Power: 241 kts.
Stall Speed
    Flaps Up: 84 kts.
    Flaps Down: 78 kts.
Rate Of Climb: 1475 fpm; 270 fpm single
Service Ceiling: 25,000 + ft.; 13,490 ft. single
Takeoff Distance
    Ground Roll: 1555 ft.
    Total Distance Over 50' Obstacle: 2643 ft.
Landing Distance
    Ground Roll: 1378 ft.
    Total Distance Over 50' Obstacle: 2427 ft.

20,000 feet. Range at that altitude and power setting is 1,076 statute miles with 888 pounds of usable fuel. Useful load of the airplane is 1,646 pounds. The Pressurized Skymaster is shown in Fig. 6-11.

The Skymaster series offers a roomy cabin with six-place seating and an instrument panel capable of housing almost every option. Figure 6-12 shows a split interior view of the instrument panel and the seating arrangement. Notice the weather radar immediately below the throttle and trim control console. The six-place seating applies to the Skymaster and Turbo Skymaster, while the Pressurized Skymaster seats a maximum of five.

Prices for the Skymaster start at $104,200, $121,000 for the Turbo Skymaster, and $159,000 for the Pressurized Skymaster. Tables 6-12, 6-13, and 6-14 provide performance data and specifications for the three planes in the Skymaster series.

CESSNA 340

The Cessna 340 shown in Fig. 6-13 is a versatile and practical airplane that combines many of the economy aspects of a light twin with the speed, comfort,and high altitude capabilities of much more expensive models. The 1,000th model recently rolled off the Cessna assembly line and offers interior styling in a variety of fabrics or leather which allows for interior customization in accordance with the buyer's specific needs.

The Model 340 offers the convenience of an "air-stair" door and an aisle to permit easy access to interior seating. This is shown in Fig. 6-14. The upper cabin door extender incorporates a gas spring actuator that replaces the guide tube and scissor assembly on earlier models.

The Cessna 340 offers a maximum speed of 280 mph at 20,000 feet and will cruise at over 260 mph at 75% power at 24,500 feet. It offers a twin-engine service ceiling of 29,800 feet and a 1,650 fpm twin-engine rate of climb at sea level. Single-engine rate of climb is 315 fpm. The 340 also has a very ample baggage allowance of 930 pounds with a useful load of over 2,000 pounds in the standard configuration.

Table 6-15 provides a list of manufacturer's performance data and specifications for the model 340 which lists at $235,950 in the standard equipped version. Factory installed instrument packages can run the price up to nearly $300,000.

Fig. 6-10 Cessna Skymaster (courtesy Cessna Aircraft Co.).

CESSNA 402

The Cessna Model 402 shown in Fig. 6-15 has been built for use as a commuter, cargo or business airplane. Equipped with two six-cylinder turbocharged engines which are fuel-injected, this aircraft has a maximum speed of 283 mph at 16,000 feet and offers a rate of climb at sea level of 1,450 fpm. With an empty weight in the standard configuration of about 4,100 pounds, the 402 has a useful load of 2,783 pounds. Passengers and crew board the aircraft through an airline-type door, adding to the overall convenience of this plane. Conversion of the plane from passenger to cargo use takes a short period of time and a large amount of items can be carried in the massive fuselage.

Baggage allowance is 1,500 pounds for the 402 which requires a total distance of about 2,500 feet to land from over a 50 foot obstacle. Total ground roll on takeoff is 1,763 feet or 2,195 feet in order to clear a 50 foot obstacle. Maximum range can extend over 1,500 miles depending upon the power setting and load configuration and many options can be ordered for specialized uses.

Figure 6-16 shows the passenger seating configuration in the wide fuselage, along with the convenient aisle between seats. This view is looking back from the pilot's seat. New interior upholstery in a variety of colors, fabrics, and leather provide a distinctive look for the 402, as does a new interior paint scheme.

Table 6-16 lists the manufacturer's performance and specification data for the 402 which lists for $236,950 in the standard equipped version and for about $290,000 with the optional Cessna Businessliner III instrumentation package.

PIPER AEROSTAR 600 SERIES

The Piper Aerostar shown in Fig. 6-17 forms a series of airplanes which offer excellent performance along with comfort in a six-place cabin. Piper advertises its Aerostar 600A as the fastest normally aspirated twin producing a cruise speed at 75% power of 253 mph and a service ceiling of 21,200 feet. This altitude of operation allows for economy in being able to fly over certain weather conditions and to take advantage of tail winds. At 55% power, the 600A has a range of over 1,350 statute miles and boasts an amazing rate of climb at sea level of 1,800 fpm.

The Model 601B is turbocharged and produces an astounding 295 mph cruise at 75% power. It is rated at a service ceiling of 30,000 feet, has a range nearly equal to the normally aspirated

Fig. 6-11. Cessna Pressurized Skymaster (courtesy Cessna Aircraft Co.).

Fig. 6-12. Cessna Skymaster instrument panel and seating configuration (courtesy Cessna Aircraft Co.).

version, and its rate of climb is nearly 1,500 fpm. It carries a useful load of 2,067 pounds.

The third Aerostar model is the 601P, which is the pressurized version with a 4.25 psi pressurization system. The Aerostar 601P is certified for flight into known icing conditions and has an operational service ceiling to 25,000 feet.

Inside, the aircraft buyer has a number of choices for interior customization. The Aerostar cabin is uniform and does not taper; so no matter where you're sitting, you're never sitting on top of anyone else. The buyer has a choice of five custom color and texture combinations in soft fabrics or leather. An optional swivel seat and work table can be ordered for business and conferencing purposes. Air conditioning can also be added.

The Aerostar 600A lists for $264,520, about $30,000 less expensive than the turbo-charged 601B. The pressurized 601P heads the list in the pricing category at $368,765. Hourly operating costs for the three models are $102.10, $107.66, and $112.30, respectively. Tables 6-17, 6-18, and 6-19 provide specifications and performance data from Piper Aircraft Corporation for their 600 Series.

PIPER NAVAJO CHIEFTAIN

Twin 350 hp Lycoming engines combined with clean aerodynamic design allow the Chieftain shown in Fig. 6-18 to deliver excellent performance and fuel efficiency. With the optional nacelle fuel tank, the Chieftain can travel nearly 1,500 statute miles while still maintaining the required IFR fuel reserve. Turbocharged engines provide a service ceiling of over 24,000 feet, and Chieftain's full de-ice package, including ice inspection lights and electric windshield allows flight into known icing conditions. This means more freedom to pick the right altitude for most efficient fuel use.

Table 6-12. Performance Data and
Specifications for Cessna Skymaster (courtesy Cessna Aircraft Co.).

Wing Span: 38 ft. 2 in.
Wing Area: 202.5 ft.^{2}
Wing Loading: 22.9 lb/ft.^{2}
Length: 29 ft. 9 in.
Height: 9 ft. 2 in.
Engine: (2) Teledyne Continental 10-360-GB, 210 bhp ⓐ 2800 rpm
Propeller: Constant speed, full feathering, 2 blades, 78 and 76 in. dia.
Fuel Capacity: 90.6 gal.
Oil Capacity: 16 qt.
Empty Weight: 2787 lb.
Maximum Weight. 4648 lb.
Maximum Useful Load: 1861 lb.
Baggage Weight: 365 lb.
Speed, Max: 172 kts.
Speed, Cruise @ 75% Power: 169 kts.
Stall Speed
      Flaps Up: 70 kts.
      Flaps Down: 61 kts.
Rate Of Climb: 940 fpm
Service Ceiling: 16,300 ft.
Takeoff Distance
      Ground Roll: 1000 ft.
      Total distance Over 50' Obstacle: 1675 ft.
Landing Distance
      Ground Roll: 700 ft.
      Total Distance Over 50' Obstacle: 1650 ft.

Table 6-13. Performance Data And Specifications For Cessna Turbo Skymaster (courtesy Cessna Aircraft Co.).

Wing Span: 38 ft. 2 in.
Wing Area: 202.5 ft.^{2}
Wing Loading: 22.9 lb/ft.^{2}
Length: 29 ft. 10 in.
Height: 9 ft. 2 in.
Engine: (2) Teledyne Continental TS10-360-HB, 210 bhp @ 2800 rpm
Propeller: Constant speed, full feathering, 2 blades.
Fuel Capacity: 90.6 gal.
Oil Capacity: 18 qt.
Empty Weight: 2899 lb.
Maximum Weight: 4652 lb.
Maximum Useful Load: 1753 lb.
Baggage Weight: 365 lb.
Speed, Max: 207 kts.
Speed, Cruise @ 75% Power: 200 kts.
Stall Speed
    Flaps Up: 70 kts.
    Flaps Down: 61 kts.
Rate Of Climb: 1160 fpm
Service Ceiling: 20,000 ft.
Takeoff Distance
    Ground Roll: 1000 ft.
    Total Distance Over 50′ Obstacle: 1675 ft.
Landing Distance
    Ground Roll: 700 ft.
    Total Distance Over 50′ Obstacle: 1650 ft.

This aircraft gets over 5.6 nautical miles (6.4 statute miles) to the gallon using engines rated at 1,600 TBO. Chieftain has 62.5 cubic feet of baggage capacity with a 2,824 pound standard useful load.

Capable of carrying up to ten people comfortably, Chieftains are often used by commuter and cargo airlines. With the commuter conversion option, changing from an eight-place executive seating configuration to a ten-place commuter configuration is fast and easy.

Maximum speed for this aircraft is 265 mph and it will cruise at 75% power at over 250 mph. Standard range at 65% power is over 1,050 statute miles, increasing to nearly 1,100 statute miles at 55% economy cruise. Takeoff over a 50 foot object is less than 3,000 feet, and the rate of climb at sea level exceeds 1,100 fpm.

Counter-rotating propellers help to eliminate the need for rudder trim during power changes. They also reduce the minimum control speed and eliminate the critical engine factor.

The Chieftain flight deck resembles that of an airliner with its overhead electrical switch panel and warning lights grouped on a central annunciator panel. Several instrument packages are available.

Useful for commercial, transport, and corporate purposes, the Chieftain sells in standard form for $377,725 and estimated hourly operating expense is $128.31 based upon this price. Table 6-20 provides performance data and aircraft specifications for this model.

CESSNA CHANCELLOR

The Cessna Chacellor shown in Fig. 6-19 is best known for its cabin-sized payload. It is a very comfortable twin-engine aircraft for business travel with a maximum useful load of 2,429 pounds. The Chancellor can cruise at 224 knots (258 mph) at 75% power and at an altitude of 24,500 feet. Under these conditions, range is 1,265 statute miles with 1,236 pounds of fuel on board.

Two Continental six cylinder engines are turbocharged and fuel-injected to deliver a 310 hp rating at 20,000 feet. These are 1,400 TBO powerplants with constant speed, full feathering,

**Table 6-14. Performance Data And Specifications
For Cessna Pressurized Skymaster (courtesy Cessna Aircraft Co.).**

Wing Span: 38 ft. 2 in.
Wing Area: 202.5 ft.^{2}
Wing Loading: 23.2 lb/ft.^{2}
Length: 29 ft. 10 in.
Height: 9 ft. 2 in.
Engine: (2) Teledyne Continental TS10-360-CB, 225 bhp @ 2800 rpm
Propeller: Constant Speed, full feathering, 2 blades
Fuel Capacity: 150.6 gal.
Oil Capacity: 18 qt.
Empty Weight: 3078 lb.
Maximum Weight: 4724 lb.
Maximum Useful Load: 1646 lb.
Baggage Weight: 365 lb.
Speed, Max: 212 kts.
Speed, Cruise @ 75% Power: 205 kts.
Stall Speed
      Flaps Up: 70 kts.
      Flaps Down: 62 kts.
Rate Of Climb: 1170 fpm
Service Ceiling: 20,000 ft.
Takeoff Distance
      Ground Roll: 945 ft.
      Total Distance Over 50' Obstacle: 1500 ft.
Landing Distance
      Ground Roll: 795 ft.
      Total Distance Over 50' Obstacle: 1675 ft.

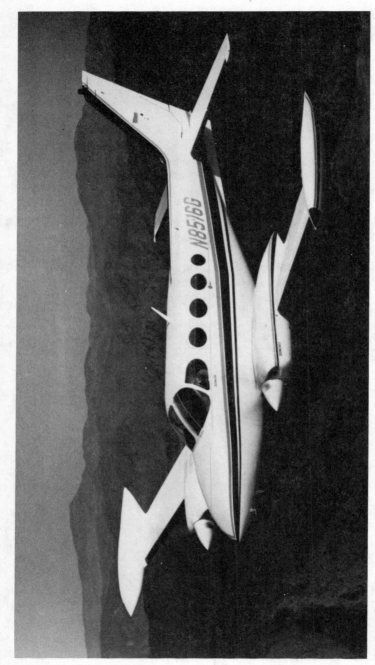

Fig. 6-13. Cessna 340 (courtesy Cessna Aircraft Co.).

Fig. 6-14. Cessna 340 passenger seating arrangement with center aisle (courtesy Cessna Aircraft Co.).

Table 6-15. Performance Data and Specifications for Cessna Model 340 (courtesy Cessna Aircraft Co.).

Wing Span: 38 ft. 1.3 in.
Wing Area: 184 ft.^{2}
Wing Loading: 32.55 lb/ft.^{2}
Length: 34 ft. 4 in.
Height: 12 ft. 7 in.
Engine: (2) Teledyne Continental TS10-520-NB, 310 bhp
Propeller: Constant speed, full feathering, 3 blade
Fuel Capacity: 102 gal.
Oil Capacity: 26 qt.
Empty Weight: 3911 lb.
Maximum Weight: 5990 lb.
Maximum Useful Load: 2114 lb.
Baggage Weight: 930 lb.
Speed, Max: 244 kts.
Speed, Cruise @ 75% Power: 229 kts.
Stall Speed
    Flaps Up: 79 kts.
    Flaps Down: 71 kts.
Rate Of Climb: 1650 fpm
Service Ceiling: 29,800 ft.
Takeoff Distance
    Ground Roll: 1615 ft.
    Total Distance Over 50' Obstacle: 2175 ft.
Landing Distance
    Ground Roll: 770 ft.
    Total Distance Over 50' Obstacle: 1850 ft.

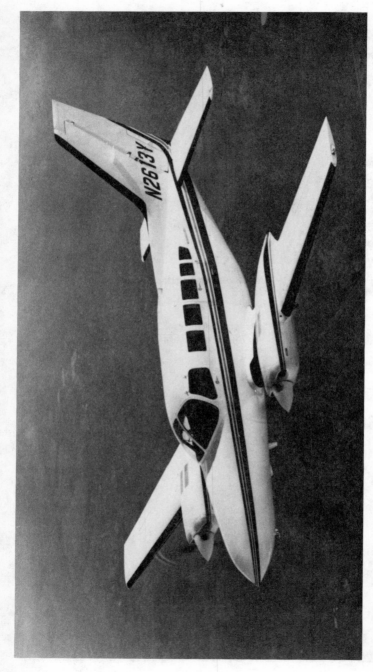

Fig. 6-15. Cessna 402 (courtesy Cessna Aircraft Co.).

Fig. 6-16. Cessna 402 seating configuration with center aisle (courtesy Cessna Aircraft Co.).

147

three-blade propellers. Twin-engine service ceiling is 30,8000 feet; while on one engine, the ceiling drops to 19,850 feet. Several seating options are available and eight persons may be carried in air conditioned comfort with a recent modification to the air distribution system which increases the air flow at the seventh and eighth cabin seat locations. An improved cabin stereo system includes pneumatic headphones as standard equipment and two overhead speakers for operation on the ground.

Chancellor II models are available with factory-installed avionics and accessories as standard equipment. Table 6-21 provides a listing of the instrumentation and other equipment which is included in the II package.

Interior styling of the Chancellor includes attractive appliques on each seat back. These are repeated on the side walls. Armrests have chrome supports and are positioned parallel to the seat bases for added comfort and styling. For exterior styling, twelve standard color combinations are available on a base of white. Table 6-22 provides performance data and specifications for the Chancel-

Table 6-16. Performance Data and Specifications
For Cessna Model 402 (courtesy Cessna Aircraft Co.).

Wing Span: 44.12 ft.
Wing Area: 225.8 ft.^{2}
Wing Loading: 30.34 lb/ft.^{2}
Length: 36.38 ft.
Height: 11.45 ft.
Engine: (2) Teledyne Continental TS10-520-VB, 310 bhp
Propeller: Constant speed, full feathering, 3 blade
Fuel Capacity: 213.4 gal.
Oil Capacity: 26 qt.
Empty Weight: 4102 lb.
Maximum Weight: 6850 lb.
Maximum Useful Load: 2783 lb.
Baggage Weight: 1500 lb.
Speed, Max: 231 kts.
Speed, Cruise @ 75% Power: 213 kts.
Stall Speed
    Flaps Up: 78 kts.
    Flaps Down: 68 kts.
Rate Of Climb: 1450 fpm
Service Ceiling: 26,900 ft.
Takeoff Distance
    Ground Roll: 1763 ft.
    Total Distance Over 50' Obstacle: 2195 ft.
Landing Distance
    Ground Roll: 1055 ft.
    Total Distance Over 50' Obstacle: 2485 ft.

Fig. 6-17. Piper Aerostar (courtesy Piper Aircraft Corp.).

149

lor, which lists for $307,470 in standard configuration. The Chancellor II is priced at $337,520; while a further option, the Chancellor III, with additional avionics, tops the list at nearly $400,000.

BEECHCRAFT DUKE

The Beechcraft Duke shown in Fig. 6-20 is a four to six-place twin-engine, turbocharged and pressurized airplane. Standard equipment includes avionics and a full compliment of engine and flight instruments. Maximum speed using the Lycoming six-cylinder engines rated at 380 hp each is 246 knots (283 mph). At the 78% power setting, the turbocharged Duke can cruise at 275 mph at 25,000 feet. It has a maximum service ceiling of 30,000 feet for twin-engine operation. Maximum single-engine service ceiling is 23,800 feet.

The Beechcraft Duke Model 60 design originally evolved from a need for a new medium twin which would offer the comfort of a pressurized cabin, turbocharged engines, optional air condition-

Table 6-17. Performance Data and Specifications
For Piper Aerostar 600A (courtesy Piper Aircraft Corp.).

Wing Span: 34.2 ft.
Wing Area: 170 ft.^{2}
Wing Loading: 32.4 lb/ft.^{2}
Length: 34.8 ft.
Height: 12.1 ft.
Cabin Width: 46 in.
Cabin Height: 48 in.
Engine: (2) Lycoming 10-540-k1J5, 290 bhp @ 2575 rpm
Fuel Capacity: 165.5 gal.
Oil Capacity: 12 qt. each
Empty Weight: 3737 lb.
Maximum Weight: 5500 lb.
Maximum Useful Load: 1788 lb.
Baggage
    Weight: 240 lb.
    Volume: 30 ft.^{3}
Speed, Cruise @ 75% Power: 220 kts.
Stall Speed, Flaps Down: 74 kts.
Rate Of Climb: 1800 fpm
Service Ceiling: 21,200 ft.
Takeoff Distance
    Ground Roll: 1550 ft.
Total Distance Over 50' Obstacle: 1950 ft.
Landing Distance
    Ground Roll: 1040 ft.
    Total Distance Over 50' Obstacle: 1840 ft.

**Table 6-18. Performance Data and Specifications
For Piper Aerostar 601B (courtesy Piper Aircraft Corp.).**

Wing Span: 36.7 ft.
Wing Area: 178 ft.^{2}
Wing Landing: 33.7 lb/ft.^{2}
Length: 34.8 ft.
Height: 12.1 ft.
Cabin Width: 46 in.
Cabin Height: 48 in.
Engine: (2) Lycoming 10-540-S1A5, 290 bhp @ 2575 rpm
Fuel Capacity: 165.5 gal.
Oil Capacity: 12 qt. each
Empty Weight: 3958 lb.
Maximum Weight: 6000 lb.
Maximum Useful Load: 2067 lb.
Baggage
    Weight: 240 lb.
    Volume: 30 ft.^{3}
Speed, Cruise @ 75% Power: 257 kts.
Stall Speed, Flaps Down: 77 kts.
Rate Of Climb: 1460 fpm
Service Ceiling: 30,000 ft.
Takeoff Distance
    Ground Roll: 1900 ft.
    Total Distance Over 50' Obstacle: 2490 ft.
Landing Distance
    Ground Roll: 1230 ft.
    Total Distance Over 50' Obstacle: 2030 ft.

ing, and luxurious interiors in a new profile of swept-back empennage styling. The production airplane utilized such modern engineering and construction methods as chemical milling of skins to remove weight without reducing strength, metal bonding and honeycomb stiffening for lightweight strength in areas of high stress, magnesium skins in the empennage and extensive use of flush riveting to provide an aerodynamically "clean" airplane.

Its Lycoming engines were designed with turbochargers rather than adding them as a "bolt-on" accessory to provide high altitude performance and maximum engine reliability. The same time-proven landing gear used on Beechcraft Bonanza and Baron airplanes was strengthened and incorporated into the Model 60 design.

The first Beechcraft Duke Model 60 was delivered in August 1968. Two years later, the Beechcraft Duke A60 was introduced with the addition of new turbocharger assemblies and exhaust ducting to improve efficiency and service life. It also featured new interior/exterior appointments.

By 1973, when the Duke B60 was introduced, 247 Beechcraft Dukes had rolled off Beech's Salina, Kansas assembly line. Interior changes were major with the third and fourth seats moved outboard to provide more width in the cabin aisle; the instrument panel glareshield was mounted in a lower position to provide improved visibility; pilot and co-pilot seat tracks were lengthened for more maneuverability; and the aft cabin floorboard was lowered to improve ease of entry.

New developments in cabin pressurization systems and pressurization controllers identical to those on the Beechcraft King Air C90 were incorporated into the Duke in 1975. Effective with airplane serial number P-365 and after, the 1976 Duke featured a second optional fuel system, increasing total usable fuel capacity to 232 gallons and range by 20% at 68% power at 15,000 feet.

By 1976, the Beechcraft Duke's direct operating costs were decreased by 25%. This was achieved by increasing the TBO for the Lycoming TIO-541-E1C4 engine by 400 hours to 1,600 hours,

Table 6-19. Performance Data and Specifications For Piper Aerostar 601P (courtesy Piper Aircraft Corp.).

Wing Span: 36.7 ft.
Wing Area: 178 ft.^{2}
Wing Loading: 33.7 lb/ft.^{2}
Length: 34.8 ft.
Height: 12.1 ft.
Cabin Width: 46 in.
Cabin Height: 48 in.
Engine: (2) Lycoming 10-540-S1A5, 290 bhp @ 2575 rpm
Fuel Capacity: 165.5 gal.
Oil Capacity: 12 qt. each
Empty Weight: 4056 lb.
Maximum Weight: 6000 lb.
Maximum Useful Load: 1969 lb.
Baggage
    Weight: 240 lb.
    Volume: 30 ft.^{3}
Speed, Cruise @ 75% Power: 257 kts.
Stall Speed, Flaps Down: 77 kts.
Rate Of Climb: 1460 fpm
Service Ceiling: 25,000 ft.
Takeoff Distance
    Ground Roll: 1900 ft.
    Total Distance Over 50' Obstacle: 2490 ft.
Landing Distance
    Ground Roll: 1230 ft.
    Total Distance Over 50' Obstacle: 2030 ft.

Fig. 6-18. Piper Navajo Chieftain (courtesy Piper Aircraft Corp.).

the highest in this class of airplane. In 1977, new developments provided a greater measure of safety, including fuel sight gauges with the long range fuel option; new cruise performance charts; and the Collins Microline computerized avionics package, now standard equipment in the Duke.

The 1978 line boasted the quietest cabin sound level ever offered due to redesigned pressurization airflow and totally new soundproofing materials used on the aft bulkheads and enclosures. Added comfort in the Duke was assured by redesigned armrests and larger seats. The new wider aisle space provided better accessibility to the cockpit area. Further safety and ease of maintenance was provided by replacement of the Ni-Cad battery with two 12-volt lead acid batteries.

A two-place couch replaced the fifth and sixth seats in 1980 and added seven inches to the width of the rear seat area. Sidewalls were redesigned to provide an additional two inches of elbow room. Armrests included a hydraulic lock so each seat back could be adjusted to suit each individual. This brings the Beechcraft

Table 6-20. Performance Data and Specifications
For Piper Navajo Chieftain (courtesy Piper Aircraft Corp.).

Wing Span: 40.67 ft.
Wing Area: 229 ft.^{2}
Wing Loading: 30.6 lb/ft.^{2}
Length: 34.63 ft.
Height: 13.0 ft.
Cabin Width: 50 in.
Cabin Height: 51.5 in.
Engine: (2) Lycoming T10-540-J2BD, 315 bhp @ 2400 rpm
Fuel Capacity: 182 gal. (236 gal. optional)
Oil Capacity: 12 qt. each
Empty Weight: 4221 lb.
Maximum Weight: 7000 lb.
Maximum Useful Load: 2824 lb.
Baggage
    Weight: 700 lb.
    Volume: 217 ft.^{3}
Speed, Max: 231 kts.
Speed, cruise @ 75% Power: 221 kts.
Stall Speed, Flaps Down: 74 kts.
Rate Of Climb: 1120 fpm
Service Ceiling: 24,000 + ft.
Takeoff Distance
    Ground Roll: 1850 ft.
    Total Distance Over 50' Obstacle: 2780 ft.
Landing Distance
    Ground Roll: 1045 ft.
    Total Distance Over 50' Obstacle: 1880 ft.

Fig. 6-19. Cessna Chancellor (courtesy Cessna Aircraft Co.).

155

Duke to 1981, where 550 of these special Beechcraft have been produced for a select market of mostly owner-flown operators.

The Duke B60 offers a useful load of 2,396 pounds. Two baggage compartments are provided with 32 cubic feet being offered in the front compartment and 28.25 cubic feet aft. Maximum weight limits are 500 pounds forward and 315 pounds in the rear. A wide range of standard equipment is offered in the base purchase price of $341,700. Table 6-23 provides the manufacturer's performance data and aircraft specifications.

GOING FURTHER

While some of the latter twins discussed are certainly designed for the commercial and corporate market, going further up the line brings us to the prop jets and pure jets. Here, we are often talking about million dollar-plus airplanes which are designed for specialized buyers. A complete discussion of these aircraft is not within the framework of this text.

Many of the twins already discussed will approach or even exceed the million dollar price tag when fully equipped with IFR instrumentation. In some rare instances, instrumentation can even bear a higher price tag than that of the aircraft into which it is installed.

SUMMARY

Twin-engine airplanes offer many, many features which are not found in single-engine aircraft. Generally speaking, their performance is superior to single-engine planes, and their safety margins are superior. When considering the safety of a twin during

Table 6-21. Listing of Instrumentation and Other Avionics Included in Chancellor II Package (courtesy Cessna Aircraft Co.).

Dual 400 Nav/Com with ARC	Cabin Pressure Control
400 ADF	Flight Instruments, Right and Panel
400 Transponder	Right Landing Light
400 DME	Economy Mixture Indicator
400B Nav-O-Matic	Emergency Locator Beacon
400 Glide Slope	Flight Hour Recorder
400 Marker Beacon	Fire Extinguisher (Hand Type)
Marker Audio Muting	Ground Service Plug
Basic Avionics Kit	Taxi Light
Audio System	Strobe Light
Avionics Cooling	Nose Wheel Fender
Antennas	Static Dischargers

Table 6-22. Performance Data and Specifications
For Cessna Chancellor (courtesy Cessna Aircraft Co.).

Wing Span: 44.12 ft.
Wing Area: 225.8 ft.^{2}
Wing Loading: 29.89 lb/ft.^{2}
Length: 36.38 ft.
Height: 11.45 ft.
Engine: (2) Teledyne Continental TS10-520-NB, 310 bhp
Propeller: Constant speed, full feathering, 3 blades
Fuel Capacity: 213.4 gal.
Oil Capacity: 26 qt.
Empty Weight: 4356 lb.
Maximum Weight: 6750 lb.
Maximum Useful Load: 2429 lb.
Baggage Weight: 1500 lb.
Speed, Max: 235 kts.
Speed, Cruise @ 75% Power: 224 kts.
Stall Speed
    Flaps Up: 82 kts.
    Flaps Down: 72 kts.
Rate Of Climb: 1520 fpm
Service Ceiling: 30,800 ft.
Takeoff Distance
    Ground Roll: 2185 ft.
    Total Distance Over 50' Obstacle: 2595 ft.
Landing Distance
    Ground Roll: 1013 ft.
    Total Distance Over 50' Obstacle: 2392 ft.

an engine outage, it should be remembered that when many twin-engine aircraft are loaded to the maximum, they are not capable of continuing for great distances on a single engine. For this reason, an engine failure is a most serious occurrence, one which can necessitate the declaration of an emergency by the pilot in command. While a twin-engine aircraft may not require both engines to be operating in order to maintain a flight, it does require twin-engine operation to fly properly and safely. To make a fair comparison between twins and singles, an engine failure on a single-engine plane most often results in emergency procedures being carried out immediately. Should one engine on a twin fail, more time is allotted to the pilot to establish just what his condition and options are. This increased time element is often adequate to allow for a near-normal return to the airport of destination or to a nearby airport along the flight route.

Some new pilots to twin-engine aircraft tend to rely too heavily upon the additional safety factors to make up for lack of piloting skills. It should be remembered that all safety precautions which apply to single-engine aircraft, such as the walk-around

Fig. 6-20. Beechcraft Duke (courtesy Beech Aircraft Corp.).

Table 6-23. Performance Data and Specifications For Beechcraft Duke (courtesy Beech Aircraft Corp.).

Wing Span: 39 ft. 4 in.	Volume: 60 ft.^{3}
Wing Area: 212.9 ft.^{2}	Speed, Max: 246 kts.
Wing Loading: 31.8 lb/ft.^{2}	Spee, Cruise @ 75% Power: 239 kts.
Length: 33 ft. 10 in.	Stall Speed
Height: 12 ft. 4 in.	Flaps Up: 81 kts.
Cabin Width: 50 in.	Flaps Down: 73 kts.
Cabin Height: 52 in.	Rate Of Climb: 1600 fpm
Fuel Capacity: 142 gal. (232 gal. optional)	Service Ceiling: 30,000 ft.
Oil Capacity: 14 qt. each	Takeoff Distance
Empty Weight: 4423 lb.	Ground Roll: 2075 ft.
Maximum Weight: 6775 lb.	Total Distance Over 50′ Obstacle: 2626 ft.
Maximum Useful Load: 2396 lb.	Landing Distance
Baggage	Ground Roll: 1318 ft.
Weight: 815 lb.	Total Distance Over 50′ Obstacle: 3065

inspection to determine the general airworthiness of the craft, apply *doubly* to twin-engine airplanes. True, there may be twice the amount of engines to keep you airborne, but there are also twice as many things that can go wrong. A single-engine aircraft is designed to perform properly under the power of a single powerplant. The twin is designed to perform properly when powered by *two* engines. The loss of an engine in either plane results in a dangerous situation. So, if you're going to fly a twin, make sure that it stays a twin for the entire length of the flight.

Chapter 7

A Trip To Your Local Airport

Perhaps one of the first things the reader might consider doing as a
potential candidate for flying lessons is to take a trip to a nearby
airport to see what flying is all about. If possible, choose a
relatively small airport where the operator or other personnel may
have more time to talk with you. More than likely, you will have
many questions which will need answers before you decide to
commit yourself to acquiring a private license.

In writing this book, the author and his staff traveled to a local
airport in Virginia near Washington, D.C. We had set up an
appointment with the FBO (Fixed Base Operator) who set aside
time to talk with us about his operation.

The first sight we had of the airport gave the impression of
utility rather than plush sophistication. The wooden buildings were
a bit weather-beaten but in a good mechanical state of repair.
These first buildings were used as emergency hangars and as
shelter for planes being serviced. One such building is shown in
Fig. 7-1. Everything from single seat aerobatic planes to light
twins could be placed within this shelter when weather conditions
would not permit outside servicing. We saw several planes with
their engine cowlings removed which were in the process of being
serviced. Others which were awaiting parts had their engines
wrapped with a weather-proofing plastic to prevent rust and the
infiltration of insects and small animals while the cowling was off.
Figure 7-2 shows the view we had as we entered the airport gate.

Perhaps the most interesting sight next to the many different
types of airplanes found at most local airports is the runway itself.

Fig. 7-1. Typical airport building used for regular maintenance and emergency hangaring of airplanes.

The Front Royal Airport operates a single, 3,000 foot paved runway lying in a roughly east/west direction. Figure 7-3 shows the view a pilot might have seconds before making his takeoff run down runway 27. Notice the marker lights which lie on either side of the paved area.

WIND INDICATORS

A short walk to the left side of the runway brought us in close range with the windsock shown in Fig. 7-4. As the wind blows, it partially inflates the elongated bag which indicates the direction in which the wind is blowing. Pilots always attempt to land *into* the wind; seeing the windsock from the air, they will attempt to land on the end of the runway toward which the end of the bag is pointing.

Another wind indication device is the tetrahedron shown in Fig. 7-5. This is a geometrical solid which rotates on a turret and has been lined with rows of lights in order to be seen from the air and at night. Due to its shape, the pointed end of the tetrahedron will always point into the wind. The pilot of an approaching aircraft will land on the runway which will most nearly allow his plane to be pointing in the same direction as the tetrahedron. This device differs from the windsock, which points in the same direction the wind is blowing. In more standard terminology, the windsock points *away* from the wind, whereas the tetrahedron point is aimed *into* the wind. Figure 7-6 shows how the windsock and tetrahedron would appear when subjected to the same wind conditions at a small airport. The direction an airplane would take on takeoff or on landing is also indicated in this drawing.

RUNWAYS

It was mentioned that this airport has but a single runway, so one might ask what a pilot would do when the wind is blowing across the runway. Figure 7-7 shows a partial crosswind, as is indicated by the windsock and tetrahedron. In this case, the pilot would land on the left end of the runway, as is referenced by this drawing, because the wind direction favors this end more than the other. There is more of a headwind on the left end of the runway than there is on the right.

Sometimes a wind may be blowing at a 90 degree angle to a runway, as is indicated in Fig. 7-8. This is a highly unusual situation, as one end or the other is almost always slightly favored at least. In the unusual condition, shown in the last figure, the pilot could safely choose either end. In most situations such as these,

Fig. 7-2. One immediately sees airplane after airplane upon entering the airport gate.

Fig. 7-3. Pilot's view of a runway shortly before takeoff.

Fig. 7-4. Windsocks are found at almost every airport.

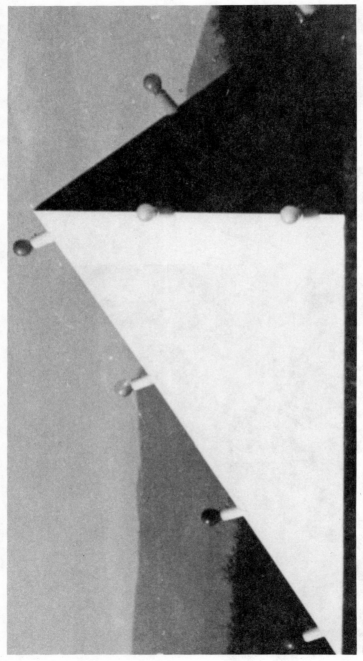

Fig. 7-5. The tetrahedron points into the wind, indicating that the pilot should land in the pointing direction.

the pilot would probably radio the airport and ask which end of the runway was the "active" one. This question simply means *which end of the runway is everyone else using?* Based on the information obtained from the airport operator, the pilot will then make a decision. To repeat, almost always, one end or the other will be favored by the wind. As a matter of fact, most runways are built after much research work has gone into the determination of the direction of a specific area's average prevailing winds. This aids everyone involved. For instance, it would not be a good idea to install a runway which runs north and south in an area where the prevailing winds blow from east to west. What would be ultimately obtained is an airport with a nearly constant crosswind. Crosswinds add to the difficulty factors in takeoffs and especially in landings, so most pilots prefer airports with runways that avoid these as much as possible.

Some areas of this country may have prevailing winds which constantly shift from one direction to another. Figure 7-9 shows some multi-runway configurations which can offset this wind direction problem. Space is often a determining factor and rarely will one see the perpendicular patterning of two runways of equal lengths. Often, one runway will be positioned in an east/west direction with the second one crossing it in a northeasterly/ southwesterly line. Any combination of this basic pattern may be used with all directions being different but in the same relationship as the example given above.

FACILITIES

Continuing our airport tour, we looked over the wide assortment of privately owned aircraft based at this facility. Figure

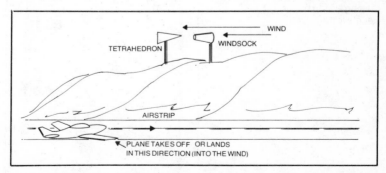

Fig. 7-6. A windsock and tetrahedron react oppositely under the same wind conditions.

167

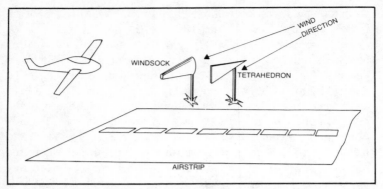

Fig. 7-7. This diagram indicates a partial crosswind (see windsock and tetrahedron). A pilot would land on the left end of the runway in this example.

7-10 shows some of the single-engine planes which are not hangared but kept at "tie-down" in an open area near the runway. Stakes are driven into the ground and surrounded by concrete to act as attachment points for ropes which are connected to the plane. Figure 7-11 shows a typical tie-down installation. Airplanes are

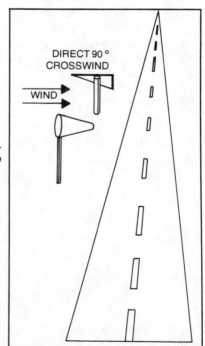

Fig. 7-8. Diagram of conditions indicating a wind blowing at a 90 degree angle to the runway.

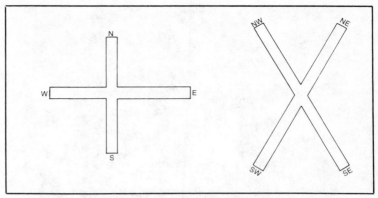

Fig. 7-9. Some airports offer multi-runway configurations similar to these.

meant to fly and sometimes those which are left on the ground untied are literally lifted by a strong headwind and overturned. A light plane is usually tethered to the ground at two tie-down points under each wing and possibly a third attached to the tail of the plane.

Peering into a newly built hangar, we spied a corporate aircraft, a Cessna 421, which was operated from the Front Royal area. The hangar had been specially built to house this aircraft. The local government, which has ultimate say over the use of their airport, would eventually get back the price of the hangar through personal property taxes which are levied on aircraft as well as automobiles.

Next stop on the tour was beneath the beacon shown in Fig. 7-12. The high intensity flashing light which is housed and supported by the tower is a visual marker to all aircraft for miles around indicating the presence of the Front Royal Airport.

After eyeballing some of the planes close up, it was time for our interview with the airport operator, so we beat a hasty retreat for the reception area, or lounge. This room is shown in Fig. 7-13. Again, it wasn't plush but it was clean, neat, and very comfortable. This is the area where transient pilots and their passengers might wait out a sudden summer storm or where a businessman might await the arrival of an industrial part flown in by private plane from the Washington, D. C. area. There was even a small, do-it-yourself snack bar where one could get a bag of chips, package of crackers, or even a microwave prepared ham sandwich. A quick glance near the ceiling revealed row after row of what appeared to be the ripped out backs of dress shirts. Each one had a name and date neatly

Fig. 7-10. Several single-engine planes are tied down at this airport.

Fig. 7-11. A tie-down block consists of a hook set in cement.

171

Fig. 7-12. The aircraft beacon shown above the building produces a high intensity flashing light.

172

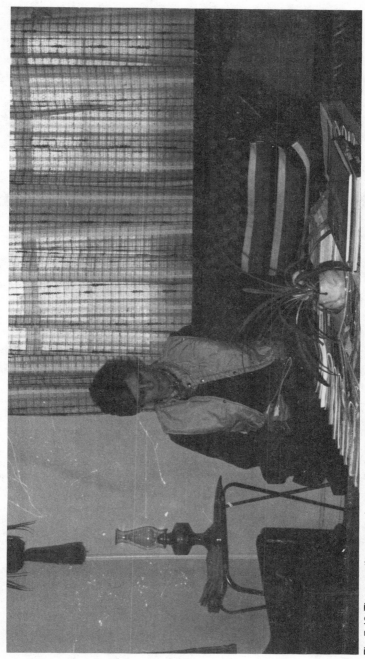

Fig. 7-13. The reception area or lounge at a local airport.

printed on it. Even a beginning pilot knows that these are the ceremonial leavings of those persons who have taken flying lessons and successfully been signed off for solo operation. This modern day ceremony is most often accomplished in a watered down manner by neatly cutting away the back of the shirt which the new pilot wore during his first solo flight. The idea is that it must be removed immediately while still soaked with the perspiration which often accompanies this maiden voyage. In olden days when men were men and pilots were warriors, the ceremony was not so civilized. Instead of scissors, two hairy hands gripped the back collar of the shirt and literally ripped it from the new pilot's back. Often, hanks of hair, dog tag chains, and small pieces of skin accompanied the removed material. It turned out that soloing pilots were so worried about this ceremony that they forgot to worry about actually soloing the plane.

There is probably very little truth to the reason behind the ceremony just discussed. The story presented here is one that has been told so many times that it has become ritual.

CONVERSATION WITH THE FBO

Our trip through the lounge carried us to the operator's office, where we met Mr. Jim Coiner, Airport Operator and owner of the Coiner Flying Service. Jim, shown in Fig. 7-14, sat behind a reasonably organized desk with a perpetual grin on his face. A very large man, one would immediately wonder just how he was able to squeeze into some of the tiny, two-place planes that he regularly piloted. After some general discussion, the interview got under way and proceeded as follows:

Author: *As a fixed base operator, you must have many duties around this airport. Would you please explain to us, in your words, what a fixed base operation is?*

Coiner: Any person who runs an individual operation in any airport, or one that encompasses the entire airport, is a fixed base operator. This business could include aircraft sales and rentals, charter flights, maintenance (both major and minor), flight instruction, ground schooling, and fueling services.

Author: *The Front Royal Warren County Airport is not a large facility, so is your business a one-man type of operation or are many people involved?*

Coiner: For an airport of this size, it just about has to be a one-family type of operation due to the normal amount of income which can be generated and to the lack of physical space. This is certainly not a one-man operation, as I depend upon family members to help out in many different areas. Other than family, I do employ a full time flight instructor. Even with the small number of personnel employed in operating this facility, I am very proud of the fact that we offer 24-hour emergency service.

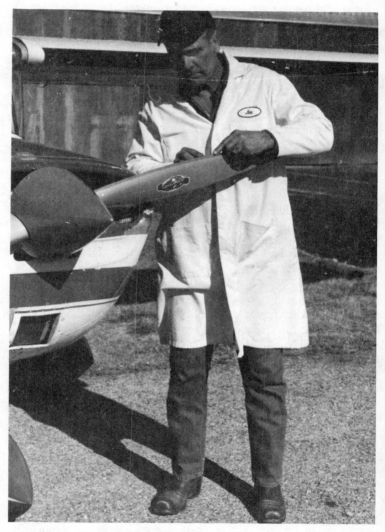

Fig. 7-14. Jim Coiner, airport operator and owner of his own flying service, guided us on a trip around the local airport.

Author: *This is a non-controlled airport. There is no FAA control tower and no Federal officials standing by. As the airport operator, what kind of control do you have at this community-owned airport?*

Coiner: There is no control over who lands and generally utilizes the airport as long as local, state and federal regulations are abided by. I am charged with operating and abiding by the rules of these three jurisdictions; however, there are some gray areas. Virginia law states that any operator has the same powers as police personnel regarding the immediate area of the airport. We have very few problems in this area.

Author: *What do you consider to be one of the problems of local airports today?*

Coiner: I think generally very few of the local people know how the airport operates or realize its usefulness to the area. There are many facilities here and an equal amount of services which a lot of local people might want to take advantage of if they only knew what we have available. We do offer tours for any interested person, such as yourself; children from the local schools sometimes take class trips to this facility to learn more about how their airport works.

Author: *I'm sure a lot of unusual things must occur at any airport. Can you give us an example of something that might be of interest to the readers?*

Coiner: There is not a whole lot of excitement in this business. However, a few years ago, the Goodyear Blimp was in this area, so I contacted the pilot by Unicom, told him about our little airport facility, and invited him to stop in sometime when he was flying a lighter aircraft. The next thing I knew, the Goodyear Blimp had entered our airspace and was shooting an approach for the runway. He didn't stop, of course, but just kept on his course over the runway, heading for Roanoke, Virginia. The pilot was just being friendly and giving us all a thrill here on the ground. Pilots are that way.

Author: *On a more serious note, Jim, as the airport operator you must have a lot of responsibilities in wintertime. How do you go about handling winter snows and freezes and their effect on the runway?*

Coiner: We have a piece of Civil Defense equipment which is a large plow that can quickly remove the snow from the runway. Once the snow depth has reached a few inches, we remove it immediately. Sometimes, we have to do this around the clock, because if too much builds up, it may get icy underneath and be impossible to remove. Last winter, we had nine inches of snow here. Other areas received even more and for a time, we were the only airport on the East Coast that I know of with a runway open. At this time, there was a man from Ohio flying to Prince George's Airport in Maryland who found himself in the awkward position of having only one hour of remaining fuel and no place to land. He radioed an FSS (Flight Service Station) which told him to contact us by Unicom, reporting that we usually kept our runway open in all kinds of weather conditions. After he landed, he told me it was the prettiest black strip he had ever seen. Icing conditions, of course, can be even worse than snow and there is really not too much we can do about it. The large airports have heaters and flame-throwers which are out of our price range and operational know-how. When ice forms on the runway, we notify Flight Service and people have to land at their own risk. If you know how to handle it, it can be done. If you don't, then you shouldn't be flying when there is any chance of these conditions developing.

Author: *How about emergency situations? Do you have many of these?*

Coiner: We have very few out-and-out emergencies. Oh, we do have people lost and short on gas now and then. We talk to them by radio and help them identify where they are by landmarks. When we find their general location, we give them a magnetic heading to the airport. Sometimes we can tell where they are by the volume with which we receive them over the local intercom. If the volume keeps increasing, we know they're coming the right way. If it's decreasing, we have them complete a 180 degree turn. It's a very simple procedure. We don't have to do it often, but we're ready when called on.

Author: *When someone comes to you and expresses an interest in learning to fly, what takes place from there?*

Coiner: The first thing we do is explain our program. Ground school is free here. We explain costs. Then, we suggest they go out and take a lesson with the instructor. If they like it or if they don't, we urge them to take one more lesson. If everything seems okay at this point, we will suggest an overall training program which will take them through solo or through a private pilot's license, depending on their desires and the amount of money they have available to put toward flying. I usually tell them after the first lesson, when they've decided that they want to continue, that the total cost for obtaining a private pilot's license by training at this airport facility is about $1400 to $1500. Some airports will offer packages considerably higher than this due to the planes and equipment they use. Some airports may be a little cheaper. Back in 1975, $1200 was considered to be about the average price of obtaining the same license; so with the inflation rate being what it is, I don't feel that today's rates are that much of an increase. Of course, all airport facilities are affected by the price of gas. Aviation gas at this airport is $1.73 per gallon, but the price can range nationwide anywhere from $1.46 to $2.00 per gallon.

Author: *I'm sure you've seen a lot of successful pilots go through the training stages at this facility. Have you noticed any kind of personality trends which might tend to make one a better pilot?*

Coiner: I see about ten to twelve students a year go through our training program. Very few drop out in the beginning stages. Those who won't go on to get the private pilot's license usually quit not too long after soloing. I guess they have learned by this time that successful piloting takes a lot of hard work and study. The initial excitement of the experience has worn off and they are not sufficiently trained to fully realize all of the many other aspects a private pilot can enjoy. Personality doesn't really enter into it, however. Anyone that is in good physical and mental condition can fly. Hearing disorders, diabetes, high blood pressure or heart disease will prevent a person from flying. Very rarely does a perfect person come along who can combine the traits needed to excel in *both* flight and ground training. I mentally divide people into two groups: those who have the capacity to retain the written information better than others and those who can learn to actually pilot the aircraft in a short period of time. Unfortunately, the group which learns the book material quickly is usually not so swift when in the pilot's seat. The group which is most proficient at learning to fly the plane often has difficulty with the written test. When a person comes along who is equally adept at both of these areas, the progression to a private pilot's license is often very rapid. Again, these persons are very rare and most of us will experience some difficulties with various stages of the training. Fortunately, all of these problems are overcome with practice, study, and plain old elbow grease.

Author: *What do you feel are the general trends in flying today?*

Coiner: There is a general trend among potential aircraft owners toward buying the older, smaller planes for their own personal flying, because they use less fuel. This makes older planes more in demand, and the new market has slowed down.

As far as the beginning pilots are concerned, there are still many, many people who want to learn to fly even though the inflation rate is so high. When people are pinched by inflation and can't buy the larger items they want, they tend to look toward something recreational. Another trend I've noticed is that of airlines moving out of the smaller airports. This means the smaller commuter airlines will be able to move into these airports and set up business. As this happens, there will be more demand to cover the corporate area of commuter travel. Eventually, this will help all aviation.

Author: *Will this mean an ever-increasing load on the FBO?*

Coiner: That's hard to say. This airport will never be overrun with too much traffic. At the same time, I think it will always be necessary to have this facility. When large corporations and industries move into rural areas, the availability of an operational local airport facility ranks number five on their lists of desirable area features for plant location.

Author: *What is the most important service that you offer at this airport?*

Coiner: Maintenance. Approximately 97 per cent of our business comes from outside of this immediate area, and 90 per cent of that is maintenance. We draw business from all around the metropolitan Washington area. The reason for this is twofold. First of all, prices are lower; and secondly, people like to come out here because of the beauty of the area and the attractions which can be enjoyed in one day. Some pilots will fly their planes into this airport for some regular maintenance; and while the plane is being worked on, they will take their family to some local underground caverns, gift shops, etc. We also allow the owner/operator to come in and help with the work—something most airports do not allow. Because of this, we have a good deal of repeat business.

Author: *How would you sum up your feelings about your part in this fixed base operation?*

Coiner: Well, you're not going to get rich, but at this juncture, you're not going to starve either. I like the business and the people who are associated with flying. Sure, I could be doing something else and make more money at it, but it wouldn't be the same. I see green kids coming in here with a dollar in their hands and a glint in the eye. Sometimes, six months later, they no longer seem like kids. They're *pilots* . . . . and pilots are pilots regardless of their age, sex, race, or religion. I like them.

SUMMARY

If possible, take a trip to your local airport. Make an appointment first, so you'll be certain of being able to talk to the right persons. If you go out on a good day, you may even be able to get in on a free five or ten minute flight around the airport just to see if you like flying.

Most operators do not object to interested persons simply hanging around, observing planes taking off and landing, watching the repair work, even serving as a gopher (you go fer this and you go fer that) when small tools are needed by the mechanic. You will probably discover after your first lesson that you are hooked on flying and will want to continue. Take it a step at a time, however. *Don't* rush things; let your instructor decide when you're ready to tackle a new challenge.

Even if you don't intend to take lessons right away, a lot of practical knowledge can be picked up simply by talking to pilots and other frequent denizens of airport lounges and hangars. This knowledge may be put to use at a later time when you are learning to fly. Don't be shy, most pilots enjoy passing along stories and advice.

To sum things up, the most difficult thing about learning to fly is actually going to the airport and deciding to do so. Plan a trip there soon. You will be surprised at what you find and extremely fascinated as well.

Chapter 8

The Cost Factor

As is the case with anything today, the cost factor of owning and flying an airplane is most important. Most persons new to aviation tend to look only at a few of the expense elements involved. Many others are not recognized immediately, but they are there and must be contended with.

In addition to the actual cost of the airplane, one must figure on rental or tie-down fees, insurance, required inspection and maintenance of the aircraft, and the avionics. FAA regulations require that 100-hour inspections be made by a certified mechanic in order to keep the aircraft flightworthy. After so many hours of flying, engines must be overhauled and are often exchanged for new engines after the hourly TBO limit is up. For instance, Piper Aircraft Corporation figures $5.98 per hour of operation of their Dakota for an engine exchange at the end of their TBO period.

Insurance for a plane such as the Dakota will cost about $1,600 yearly. This includes $1,364 for a $250 deductible hull coverage. Half million dollar single-limit liability insurance will cost an additional $280 per year. Add this figure to an average of $1,200 per year for hangar rental and the total annual fixed expense is about $2,844 for a plane in this category. The fixed expense is what you would be charged whether you flew your plane or not during that year.

Now, we have to look at the assumed purchase price of a new Dakota at $70,770. This price, of course, is equivalent to that of a very nice home in most rural areas of the United States. Buying an airplane is completely different, however, as the financing of this amount of money is normally handled over a five to seven year period, although some companies and institutions may go as long as ten years. Interest rates vary with 18% being the norm at the time of this writing.

According to Piper, the estimated resale value of the aircraft under discussion after seven years of ownership and at a use factor of 500 hours per year is $42,462. Based on these figures, the net investment expense would be $28,308 over this period of time. This, of course, assumes that you had $70,770 in the bank and didn't have to borrow it at interest. Using the $28,308 figure, the net investment expense per year is $4,044, or $8.08 per hour of operation when 500 hours are put on the plane annually.

This figure must be added to the total annual fixed expense of $2,844 and then you must add about $40.00 per hour for the actual operation of the airplane and for the maintenance procedures which must be pro-rated on an hourly basis. Of this figure, over half is allotted for fuel at an average price of $1.75 per gallon. If you own a business, these figures probably won't sound too astounding. However, if you're like most people who work at a 9 to 5 job, the financial responsibility of owning an airplane would seem to take on rather astounding proportions. Don't lose heart.

PARTNERSHIPS

Most ordinary people cannot afford the price of singly owning a new aircraft in this price category, which is not extremely high as aircraft prices go. However, there are a large number of folks who might be able to form a partnership with three, four or even five other pilots in order to make aircraft ownership practical. Now, the fixed expenses are divided by the number of persons in your partnership. Everybody comes up with an equal amount of money to purchase the aircraft. Divided six ways, each share would be about $12,000 to purchase the Piper Dakota outright. Assuming the estimated retail value in seven years of about $42,000, each partner would receive $7,000 when the plane was sold. For hangar rental and insurance, each partner would pay a little less than $500 annually.

At this stage of the discussion, things may be beginning to look a bit better. One might assume that after the initial $12,000 investment (of which you're likely to get back over half when the plane is resold), the owners only have to worry about $500 each per year to maintain their 1/6th ownership in the aircraft. This is the annual fixed expense per person. This assumption is absolutely correct to *own* the plane, but flying it is going to cost you more. Piper figures a total operating expense per hour of $39.37, but this includes $5.69 per hour to cover the hangar rental and insurance. Assuming this has already been taken care of, the remainder is $33.68 per hour. This is the *minimum* you would have to pay to fly the aircraft you own a part of for one hour. All the others partners would have to do the same thing as they took their turns piloting the aircraft.

You're probably saying to yourself now, "Why should I own an aircraft when I still have to pay the equivalent of an hourly rental whenever I fly?" The answer is that this hourly cost is much cheaper than what you would have to pay to rent the same aircraft from another owner. As a matter of fact, based on all the figures, an owner would have to charge $86.82 per hour of operation in order to break even on all the fixed and variable expenses involved in making that aircraft available for rental. This includes purchase price, fuel, and all of the factors previously discussed. The figure quoted does not include a profit margin.

It is here that rentals should be discussed in a different light. Five hundred hours per year is a lot of flying time even for five or six partners. There are going to be times when far less than 500 hours of use is obtained. This will, of course, depend on the owners and nature of aircraft use. Any time the plane is not being used by any of its owners, it can be rented out. Many airports will handle this for the owners for a minimal expense. Even if more hours than we calculated are put on the airplane yearly, the profits made from rentals can completely offset this added cost with a surplus remaining. Even though the engine will need to be replaced sooner by higher usage, that cost is built into the hourly operating expenses. An aircraft engine can suffer permanent damage from *lack* of use. Planes which are rarely flown often suffer oxidation problems in the engine and may not last for the entire TBO. Regular use tends to keep the powerplant at top operational efficiency over its expected lifetime.

For business ownership of the Piper Dakota under discussion, tax savings become a large factor. Most of the expenses remain exactly the same and the benefit of tax write-offs will be a large consideration in the initial purchase. Table 8-1 is a reprint of the Piper Aircraft Corporation Operating Economics Guide for the Dakota (PA-28-236). This details the overall estimated aircraft ownership and operating expense based on an ownership for seven years at 500 hours of use annually. These figures are based on 100% business usage.

Table 8-1. Piper Aircraft Corp. Supplies an Estimated Aircraft Ownership and Operating Expense Guide With Each of Their Airplanes (courtesy Piper Aircraft Corp.).

ESTIMATED AIRCRAFT OWNERSHIP AND OPERATING EXPENSE

TOTAL OPERATING EXPENSE (SCHEDULE I)

Type Aircraft   1981 DAKOTA (PA-28-236)   Business Usage   100%

Assumed Hours Per Year   500

Assumed Years of Ownership   7

	ESTIMATED EXPENSE (A)	ESTIMATED EXPENSE NET OF TAX SAVINGS (B)
Assumed Purchase Price	$ 70,770	
Estimated Resale Value	$ 42,462	
Expense of Asset	$ 28,308	$ 28,308
Tax Savings:		
Less 46% Tax Bracket (C)	---	($ 13,022)
Less 10% Investment Tax Credit (D)	---	($ 7,077)
Net Investment Expense	$ 28,308	$ 8,209
Net Investment Expense Per Year	$ 4,044	$ 1,172
Net Investment Expense Per Hour	$ 8.08	$ 2.34
Operating Expense/Hour - Schedule II	$ 39.37	$ 21.25
Travel Expense Per Hour	$ 47.45	$ 23.59
Travel Expense Per Nautical Mile 132 Knots Block Speed at 65% Power	$ .359	$ .179
Travel Expense Per Seat Nautical Mile		
2 Seats	$ .179	$ .089
3 Seats	$ .119	$ .059
4 Seats	$ .089	$ .045

Fuel Consumption - Nautical Miles Per Gallon 11.28 (Statute miles per gallon 12.98) @ 65% Cruise Power & 11,500 Feet P.A.

(A) Before Tax Savings.
(B) This column is presented for example purposes only and it should be understood that all tax situations can vary significantly and your tax advisors should be consulted.
(C) Reflects Federal Tax savings only.
(D) Providing maximum tax limitation has not been exceeded.

USED AIRPLANES

As was mentioned earlier in this text, many private pilots are taking full advantage of the used aircraft market to become owners. Excellent buys can be had for less than $30,000 in this market, with some planes costing less than $10,000. The type of aircraft, its age, the remaining hours left on the engine or engines, as well as the overall condition of the plane, will determine the asking price. These are the buys that would seem to be most attractive to both individual owners and partnerships alike.

Unlike buying a used car, the purchase of a formerly owned aircraft is not such a risky undertaking. The FAA requires that logs be kept on maintenance and other procedures, so a new owner will be buying these log books as well to keep future records. One of the first things a person should do when considering the purchase of a used aircraft is to examine the log. You will find a complete record of the aircraft's operational life, including any repairs that were made. If you should see, for instance, that the landing gear had to be completely replaced, you might immediately ask why this had to be done. Was the plane damaged in a landing? Was there other damage to the plane resulting from the failure of the gear? You might also look to see if the propeller was overhauled after a certain number of use-hours.

The log book will tell you a lot about the airplane but may tell you even more about the previous owner or owners. If certain maintenance procedures were not performed on a regular basis, this may show in the written record. By scrutinizing the aircraft log, you will probably be able to tell whether or not it was religiously maintained. If enough abuses show up, then it might be best to look elsewhere for your purchase. On the other hand, if the log indicates the plane was treated with kid gloves by its owner, then even a craft with a lot of use-hours may be an excellent buy.

Beware of purchasing planes whose logs are incomplete. When whole sections are missing, this could be a sign of an unscrupulous seller trying to hide certain facts. These may make the difference between the purchase of a sturdy airplane which will provide you many years of relatively trouble-free operation and one which will mean difficulties and amplified expense.

It is not difficult to locate used airplanes even in rural areas. You might start by taking a trip to a nearby airport and asking the fixed base operator if he knows of any planes for sale. It is a fact among most aircraft owners that one is never satisfied with the plane he or she presently owns. Due to the price of planes today, an owner must often settle for a little less than he originally desired. Unless an owner is firmly attached to an aircraft for sentimental or other reasons, he or she will often entertain the idea of selling the present "bird" in order to move up the scale to a slightly better aircraft. During our trip to the airport, we witnessed what is often seen when you nose around long enough. Figure 8-1 shows a fixed gear single-engine aircraft which has a For Sale sign in the window along with a phone number to enable all interested parties to contact the owner. This is just about what you might find at a used car lot. A check with the FBO supplied us with information about two other planes that were definitely for sale and three others which he thought could be bought if the right deals were offered to their owners. He even offered to discuss selling one of his Cessna 150 training planes. He would use the money to replace it with a newer model. This experience brings out a very important point—it is a very easy to find used aircraft for sale. A checking glance at any bulletin board available at an airport will most likely produce pictures of other aircraft for sale or rent, along with the phone numbers and/or addresses of their owners.

Another excellent source of used aircraft can be found through various publications. There are several out that are equivalent to "Used Aircraft Buyers Guides." They are published by companies which make their money by selling advertising space to brokers, manufacturers and private aircraft owners. These publications should provide you with hundreds of used aircraft possibilities. Also, ads may be found in the back section of most of the flying magazines. These publications and magazines can usually be found in the lounges of all airports. The FBO will most likely be glad to name off a few other sources for you as well.

Fig. 8-1. Browsing around an airport will often turn up aircraft that are quite obviously for sale by their owners.

In researching this book, the author picked up a copy of *Trade-A-Plane*. This is a newspaper-like publication which comes out thrice monthly and contains thousands of ads from companies and individuals who have all types of aircraft and aircraft accessories for sale. In looking through these publications, it is necessary to know what some of the abbreviations mean. Following is a list of common abbreviations and their meanings:

TT	:	Total Time
SMOH	:	Since Major Overhaul
SPOH	:	Since Partial Overhaul
TTAF	:	Total Time Airframe
TTAE	:	Total Time Airframe and Engine
SCMOH	:	Since Complete Major Overhaul

These are terms which mostly describe time of use on the engine and/or airframe. For example, you might see an ad which reads, "Cessna 172: 3450 TT, 400 SMOH." This would mean that the Cessna 172 aircraft had been flown a total of 3,450 hours but the current engine has only 400 hours on it since the last major overhaul. Twin engine models may be advertised as follows: "1968 Piper Aztec. 3,500 TT, 500 SMOH Left, 250 SMOH Right." This description indicates the aircraft has been flown a total of 3,500 hours, the left engine has been flown 500 hours since the last major overhaul, while the right engine has been flown 250 hours since overhaul.

The Trade-A-Plane publication is an education for the reader as to what's available in the new and used aircraft market. In looking through the pages, we discover not only used single and twin engine airplanes, but helicopters, homebuilt aircraft, flight jackets, instruments and a myriad of other associated parts and equipment. Using the Cessna 172/Skyhawk as an example, it was found that this plane, which sells new for about $35,000 standardly equipped, can be purchased used for a cost of about $10,000 and up. This will, of course, depend upon the year, hours flown, instrumentation, and general condition. For example, one ad reads: "80 Cessna Skyhawk, 440 TT, Nav/Pac, Glideslope, Strobes, List $42,684, Reduced to $29,950, 100% Financing." This particular plane is a reasonably equipped newer model with only 440 hours of total time on a 2,000 hour engine. It still has close to 1,500 hours of time left on the engine before an overhaul is mandated. For many, it is probably a much better deal than a new model which, similarly equipped, would cost close to $43,000. Another ad reads: "1976 Skyhawk II, Full IFR, 1,800 TTAE, Well-Maintained, Good Condition. $15,500." This plane is inexpensive compared with a new model and is equipped for instrument flight. With the high time on the engine, it will soon need a major overhaul. This could cost in excess of $5,000, so a potential buyer must take this into account.

One thing the used aircraft buyer must watch out for is aircraft which have unusually *low* total time for their ages. For instance, if you saw an ad for a 1969 plane with only 450 hours on it, one would have to wonder just how well maintained this plane is after being flown less than 35 hours per year. This almost amounts to keeping the plane stored for most of its life. Has rust set in from under-use? Have the internal components begun to oxidize? Was the plane damaged and left to sit for many years? At first glance, this might seem to be an excellent buy because of the low time, but engines which are left to sit for long periods of time rarely reach their expected TBOs. A complete major overhaul may be necessary right from the start. Airplanes need constant care, like any other means of transportation, and neglect can quickly take its toll. On the other hand, the plane may have been professionally stored and maintained due to an illness or some other factor and could *potentially* be a good buy. Both of these possibilities must be considered. A thorough inspection by a qualified aircraft mechanic whom you may know to be trustworthy would certainly be indicated when considering the purchase of an aircraft in this category. The same should apply to any good used aircraft you buy, regardless of its apparent condition.

As is the case with buying a used car, used airplanes cost more if you have to go through a middleman. This would include the broker or dealer whose business is often advertised in used aircraft publications. The extra expense may be well worth it, as guarantees may also be included in the asking price. The least expensive way to go is to buy the used plane directly from the owner. This assumes that the aircraft has all of its engine and airframe logs intact.

Many airports may have dealers located on the premises who are in the used aircraft business. If the operator or operators also provide maintenance services and sell aviation fuel, you may be able to get a reduced price if you can convince these sellers that you will be using their facilities quite a bit. They will count on getting back any price reductions offered to you through your use of the airplane when you purchase fuel and service from them.

AIRCRAFT LEASEBACK

For many people, the next best thing to the ownership of an aircraft is a leaseback arrangement. This starts by purchasing an aircraft from a dealer, so *you do own* the plane. The difference comes in when you immediately lease the plane back to the dealer. He then rents the aircraft to other pilots and gets about 20% of the rental fee while you get the rest. This arrangement was discussed earlier but not in great detail. The leaseback offers ideal economic factors for those aircraft owners who don't use their planes every day. The pilots who are renting *your* plane are actually helping to pay for it. One difficulty which may be encountered is availability. It is sometimes quite frustrating to be unable to fly *your own* plane, owing to the fact that it has already been rented for that time or day.

Businessmen will be glad to know that, as aircraft owners, they are still qualified for the tax benefits associated with business uses of an aircraft. By taking full advantage of the tax benefits only an owner can enjoy, along with the rental income, leaseback can be one of the best ways to purchase an aircraft.

There are disadvantages other than the unavailability mentioned earlier. For one thing, it will cost considerably more to insure the plane due to the numbers of people who will be flying it. Also, the plane will be used more than if the owner were flying it exclusively, so maintenance costs will be much higher.

Leaseback is something that should be explored with your aircraft dealer, taking into account your intended uses of the aircraft and tax write-off needs. If possible, talk with aircraft owners who have been involved in a leaseback arrangement. Get their opinions and ask about any hidden costs or other burdens which may be involved.

LEASING

If you decide that leaseback is not for you, you might consider a standard lease on an aircraft without actually buying it. Today, many lease their automobiles rather than buying them outright. These leases can take many different forms, with the automobile being turned back into the dealer after one to three years, the automobile being purchased at the end of the lease period for a small amount of money, or with it being replaced by a new model at set intervals of time.

The attractive feature of any lease is that it does not require a large capital outlay at the onset. Normally, bank loans do not have to be obtained and the lease can be terminated, often with a substantial penalty, at any time. Many forms of leasing can be looked on as renting over a set period of time. Leases differ from rentals in that the latter usually have no set ending dates. Leasing is normally set up for a specific time period.

Leasing can be an ideal arrangement for many companies and individuals if the plane is to be used for business purposes. It is a compromise between renting and outright ownership which offers a high degree of flexibility. Too many persons, however, do not take full advantage of all leasing has to offer because of a lack of knowledge about the overall processes involved. The author looks at aircraft leasing as *buying the ownership of the plane for a specified period of time*. Many persons tend to look at this arrangement as a rental, but most of us think of monthly rentals as being fixed and non-negotiable. This is not true, especially when leasing is involved. Again, think of leasing as out-and-out ownership of a plane, but only for a fixed period of time. The dealer is naturally going to try to make as much money as possible from this transaction and you, as the lessor, should attempt to save yourself as much money as you can. In other words, the quoted lease price that you first receive is often not the *best* price at which the plane can be had. The solution is to negotiate (haggle) with the dealer in an attempt to arrive at a monthly fee which will be satisfactory to both parties. There is a substantial profit margin built into most leases, so a dealer has a lot of leeway in what he can settle for. Come back with an alternate figure to this first asking price. Most likely, the dealer will make a counter-offer. This may be somewhere between his original asking price and your counter-offer. The process may end here or may be carried even further depending upon your feelings about the asking price currently being discussed. With the multitude of aircraft dealers and planes available, "horse trading" is very much a part of aircraft leasing.

AIRCRAFT RENTALS

The majority of private pilots in the United States rent their aircraft. For these persons, renting is the most economical way to go for their own flying characteristics and needs. There are many costs involved in aircraft ownership and leasing which are circumvented by hourly rentals. The best thing is that as a renter, you're not responsible for maintenance and repairs on the craft you fly. There are no hidden charges. If a plane rents for $35.00 an hour, then that's what you pay . . . that's *all* you pay. We are referring here to the standard "wet" rentals, which include fuel, oil, and all the accessories to make the plane go. Dry rentals are also available which do not include fuel and oil. These are often offered to persons who may wish to rent a plane for several days and assume the variable costs themselves. These are subtracted from the fixed costs which are charged to the renter using this procedure.

Hourly rentals can most often be thought of as fixed in price. Charges are based on the number of hours the plane is actually used. The clock starts as soon as the engine is activated, so you pay the same rate for the five minutes it may take you to taxi to the end of the runway as you would for five minutes of actual flying time. By strictly adhering to the rules of wet rental, if you were to rent a plane to fly to a distant city an hour away, park the plane at your destination, conduct five hours of business and then fly home again, you would be charged for only two hours of rental time. This would apply even though the plane was away from its home airport for a total of seven hours. Under these conditions, however, the renter would probably ask (and rightly so) for an additional fee to cover the unavailability of the aircraft for the seven hour period. A mutually agreeable charge can usually be arrived at through negotiation. Since the uses of aircraft are many and varied, most persons who rent aircraft have learned to be flexible in making individual arrangements. Some persons are able to rent an airplane for an excursion covering many days at quite reasonable rates. These take into account the actual time the aircraft is flown, as well as the period for which the plane was at your disposal. Obviously, total charges for such usage would be dependent upon the normal number of rentals the owner could expect to obtain during the time you need to use the aircraft. Total cost would probably be less in off-peak flying periods.

When planning an aircraft rental for an hour, a day or even a week, always make arrangements well ahead of time so that a plane will be available when you need it. Even in small airports, it is not always possible to drop in unexpectedly and be able to rent a plane within a few minutes' time.

One serious drawback to certain types of rentals should be considered and fully understood before you ever set foot in the plane. Find out what your personal liability may be regarding use of the aircraft. Planes are required to have liability insurance, but this often applies only to the owner. It may not be extended to you.

Before renting, always find out if there is liability coverage and how much. If the figure is too low, you could be left owing a large amount of money should a mishap occur. If the aircraft is damaged during your use, the owner could come back on *you* to pay the repair bill. Even if the insurance company pays for repairs, they may still try to recoup their losses by taking the pilot in command at the time of the mishap to court. If damage is sustained by the aircraft you are flying and no others, the repair bill could be many thousands of dollars; but if damage is sustained to many aircraft by a mishap in your rented plane, the costs could be in the millions of dollars.

Fortunately, personal liability insurance for aircraft pilots is available often for less than $100.00 yearly. In the author's opinion, purchase of such a policy is money well spent for anyone who intends to regularly fly rented aircraft.

Also note that even though you (as pilot) are only renting the plane, this *does not* relieve you of the responsibility of insuring that the aircraft is in safe operating condition. You should pre-flight and inspect a rented airplane just as if it were your own, and you should do this *every time*.

YOUNG PEOPLE TAKE HEART

Rentals are about the least expensive way to fly compared to all of the other methods discussed in this chapter, at least regarding the immediate capital outlay aspects. You must add $8 to $12 per hour for dual flight time with an instructor when trying for your student or private pilot's license. Admittedly, for many persons, especially the young beginner, who has not yet made a financial mark for him or herself in the world, the prospect of this $35.00 or more per hour is quite a burden. But if you really want to fly, you will probably find a way.

One of the best methods to overcome the training cost factor is to exchange aircraft rental and instructor's fees for services rendered. The author can still remember a time in his youth when he walked into the local airport and asked the FBO if he needed any help. This was largely a one-man operation and there were many odd jobs to be performed. The FBO said he could use all kinds of help but really couldn't affort to hire on anyone, especially a kid who had absolutely no experience. His gruff nature was immediately turned philanthropic when the author told him he would be willing to work in exchange for flying lessons. For an entire summer, planes were fueled, floors were swept, and trash cans emptied just for the chance to fly. The FBO held me to two lessons per week for the first two weeks (minimum wage at this time was less than $1.00 an hour), but after this period, he took a liking to me and allowed me to fly much more often. Through this experience, I got a veritable formal education in airplanes, maintenance, and operations of an airport. Because of this, the pay was actually immeasureable and far outweighed the actual flight time earned during this summer.

This is just one way to go about it. There are many others. A friend of the author's was an advertising executive at a local radio station. In exchange for instruction through being signed off solo, the FBO was given free radio advertising. The student was charged the standard rate for rental and instruction and the FBO was charged an equal amount, at standard rates, for the radio advertising. The friend exchanged a piece of electronic equipment with the radio station manager for the advertising which he received as a discount. No money actually changed hands, but the student was signed off solo, the FBO picked up additional students from the advertising, and the radio station got a piece of test equipment it badly needed. All parties were happy because no one was burdened by this tri-lateral arrangement. Note, however, that the IRS considers such barter deals as taxable income at their fair market value.

Too many persons feel that flying is a pursuit of only the rich, those who don't have to worry about money. This is absolutely untrue. Flying more often involves the resourceful, those folks who know how to *save* money by finding the most *efficient* ways of *spending* it (or the easiest ways of not spending it). True, if you have money to burn, you may not have to work as hard in learning the techniques required during the precious hours of instructional time allotted to you, but students who do not make every flying moment count often take many hours to become licensed, and even then often do not make outstanding pilots. The opportunity to learn to fly is a precious privilege, one that should be taken with utmost seriousness owing to the overall good it does for the individual and for the flying community.

SUMMARY

To make the most efficient use of money spent toward aircraft ownership, leasing, renting and instruction, the flying buff must understand all of the options which are open. This chapter has touched on many of them and in enough detail so that intelligent questions may be asked of various manufacturers, dealers, and

FBOs. I think you will find that, generally, most people involved in any aspect of flying are reputable and helpful. But beware! As in any profession or pursuit, there are those who are waiting to take advantage of anyone they can. If you question the ethics of anyone you attempt to do business with, back off and take a studied look. It's a good idea to check out the fellow's reputation by talking with others who have done business with him in the past. Don't try to impress someone in the business with *your* knowledge of what *they* have been involved with for years. Any question you have is an intelligent one and necessary to your continued pursuit of flying. Only the foolish will show their true ignorance by not asking the necessary questions. The disreputable faction in the flying business will pick up on this immediately and take advantage of you. Make certain you get satisfactory answers to your questions. If you don't, ask someone else.

Flying is for everyone, whether young, old or in between. Those of substantial income may not have to be as resourceful as those of us who make average salaries, but all of us have the capabilities, financial and otherwise, to get that private pilot's license and a craft to use it in by some means or other. A common sense approach by all factions discussed will certainly bring about the most suitable means of attaining this mutually shared goal.

Chapter 9

The Personal Helicopter

Two decades ago, many prognosticators who felt they were familiar enough with flying to predict future trends were spreading the word that in twenty years the flying machine would be as much a part of the lives of everyday people as the automobile was in the early fifties. Many scientific journals printed articles on garage-kept airplanes with the idea that the average housewife might fly off to the supermarket in some futuristic aircraft to perform the daily shopping chores. A chicken in every pot and an aircraft in every garage seemed to be the slogan of the day.

Many of these predictions were founded in little knowledge of the physical requirements of airplanes. The more knowledgeable predictions came from those who realized that the space requirement for even a futuristic airplane would most certainly be beyond the reach of the average homeowner. They predicted the helicopter to be the Chevy of the future. This seemed more reasonable due to the fact that this type of aircraft needs no runway what with its vertical takeoff and landing capabilities.

Both groups had one thing in common—they were both *wrong*. True, the airplane of today is a much more versatile machine and offers many features unheard of in 1950. However, it certainly doesn't live up to the prediction of the same utility as an automobile. Likewise, one doesn't see too many garage-kept helicopters carrying the next door neighbor to the golf course from a backyard pad.

One company manufacturing aircraft today must have heeded some of those old predictions, because they make and sell what

Fig. 9-1. The Scorpion 133 helicopter (courtesy RotorWay Aircraft, Inc.).

could truly be described as a garage-kept aircraft. It's called the Scorpion 133 and is a true helicopter of diminutive proportions. Shown in Fig. 9-1, the Scorpion 133 is affordable, convenient, and would even be practical for a wide range of business and personal uses.

To get away from the purely technical aspects of this aircraft, the Scorpion 133 is darned interesting. It's a fairy tale come true. To many of us, it brings back memories of those old Buck Rogers movies, and anyone with a bit of imagination can visualize the awe of neighbors when they see you coming in for a landing.

An exploded diagram of the Scorpion 133 is shown in Fig. 9-2. This is not some dangerous toy which has been put together in a haphazard manner. It's a true helicopter which offers the convenience of vertical takeoffs and landings, hovering, a speed of 80 to 90 mph, and a price of less than $25,000. Besides all this, it looks futuristic. The streamlined cabin enclosure is constructed of lightweight fiberglass and provides maximum visibility through the large windscreen. The sleek appearance is more than attractive; it's extremely functional and results in improved flight performance and stability.

The powerplant is a four-cylinder, four-stroke, horizontally opposed water-cooled aircraft engine designed by RotorWay Aircraft, Inc. specifically for the Scorpion helicopter. This in itself is unusual, as the private aircraft industry has usually had to rely upon someone else to manufacture their powerplants. In effect, they had to make do with adaptations of some existing designs. Some of the first Scorpion helicopters were powered by a two-stroke engine, but with the introduction of the Scorpion 133, RotorWay had taken the bull by the horns and designed *an engine* for *an aircraft* rather than the other way around. The right horsepower to weight ratio, rpm, torque curve, fuel economy, and physical size were incorporated into the design of the engine for the Scorpion airframe.

The four-stroke engine is much more reliable and efficient than its two-stroke predecessor. It's also cleaner. The horizontally opposed design provides for much smoother operation and greater power. The previous engine was air cooled, while the current powerplant is liquid cooled for lower operating temperatures and a longer life. Dry weight of the four-stroke powerplant is 165 pounds. RotorWay has been successful in eliciting one hp for every cubic inch of engine displacement: 133 hp from 133 cubic inches. Fuel consumption is 7.4 gallons per hour, and fuel capacity is 10

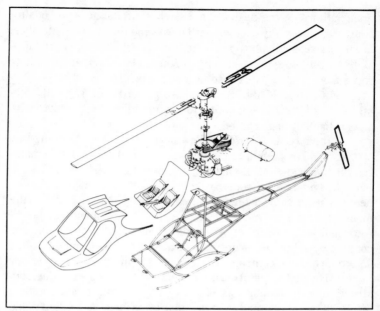

Fig. 9-2. Exploded diagram of the Scorpion 133 helicopter (courtesy RotorWay Aircraft, Inc.).

gallons. Another practical point is evident in the fact that this powerplant uses 92 octane automotive gasoline. Obviously, the Scorpion 133 is not designed for long non-stop trips. At 7.4 gallons per hour and a 10 gallon tank, most pilots would pretty much limit their trips to a maximum of about an hour's duration before refueling. With the correct wind conditions, one should be able to safely muster 100 miles per trip.

Standard list price for the Scorpion is $16,675. This may be confusing to the reader who, by this time, has become accustomed to the prices of the aircraft formerly discussed, these costing $30,000 or more. The secret behind the low cost of the Scorpion is that *you build it yourself*. The base price is for the major components and smaller parts which are put together to form a safe, efficient helicopter. In other words, it's a kit. This may come as a surprise, but for years many different types of aircraft have been available in kit form and may cost many times the original price when resold in assembled form. You save many thousands of dollars by putting in the man hours required for this assembly.

No, you don't have to be an experienced aircraft mechanic to build the Scorpion 133. It is not a simple task by any stretch of the imagination; but the design, engineering, production, and quality control at RotorWay coupled with one of the finest assembly plans in the business will allow most individuals with normal mechanical skills to complete the assembly in 500 to 600 hours. If specialists were used to handle this assembly at the factory, another $10,000 could easily be added to the purchase price. RotorWay sells only kits and many have been built and are providing their owners with safe, reliable transportation.

In their book, *The RotorWay Story*, RotorWay Aircraft, Inc. states: "The availability of new and improved construction materials has unquestionably advanced the state of the art of rotary-wing design. The helicopter is comprised of several basic components. The airframe is the fundamental unit. To this is attached the main rotor mast and motor mast and rotor blades along with the tail rotor and tail rotor drive. An engine is mounted in the frame and coupled by some means of transmission to the main and tail rotor. There are also controls along with an instrument panel for monitoring flight operations. Conventional helicopter frame construction normally consists of a complex network of small tubes, many intersections and a great deal of associated braketry and construction detail.

"In the Scorpion, frame construction has been greatly simplified by using large diameter tubes. Two main tubing members form the basic frame structure. Simple braces are added providing a structure to which all of the additional mechanism of the helicopter is readily attached. The concept of using large diameter tubing rather than small tubes, and many of them, also makes the construction of the Scorpion frame very adaptable to the RotorWay Educational Program. A weldment around a large diameter tube is always much stronger than a short weld around a small tube. The construction of the Scorpion frame also incorporates a rigid rotor pylon area so that in the event of roll over, an extremely sturdy cage completely protects the pilot.

"Helicopter mechanism is built up of several basic units: the main rotor and rotor system, the drive train to the main rotor, the drive train to the tail rotor and the tail rotor system. Regardless of the design philosophy of any particular helicopter, a rotary-wing machine is a precision piece of equipment. Machined components in the various mechanical units must be built to a high standard of excellence with rigorous quality control procedures being used as the construction stage progresses. Close tolerance fits for items such as bearings are extremely important. Precision holes providing for perfect alignment of the rotor blade pitching axis are of extreme importance. Rigid heat treat specifications must be maintained and plating processes such as anodizing of aluminum parts and cadmium plating of metal parts must be carefully controlled. If there is to be any interchangeability of parts, very precise jigs and fixtures must be designed. Without a precision fixture, there can be no hope of ever replacing any single part.

"There are three control systems functioning in any helicopter. These units consist of the cyclic, collective and directional controls along with some type of throttling device. Controls must be designed for long life and smooth, precise operation. All controls in the Scorpion 133 function with precision bearings and quality dampening devices.

"The enclosure for any rotary-wing design must meet certain performance criteria. The enclosure must be light, aerodynamically well designed, easy to fabricate, and as inexpensive as possible. Aluminum, fiberglass, and plexiglass have been used extensively in past helicopter cabin design. In the case of the Scorpion, a minimum fiberglass enclosure was chosen. A plexiglass windscreen is used which may be easily formed from a flat sheet of plexiglass and simply attached to the very eye-appealing and aerodynamic Scorpion cabin.

"Quality control in the area of fiberglass construction is also of great importance. Only the best methods are employed by RotorWay technicians. Since strength and weight are factors of extreme importance, only the hand lay-up method is used. All excess resin is squeezed out of the material, leaving the part light with a great degree of impact resistance and overall structural strength."

HOMEBUILDING-THE MONEY SAVING APPROACH

Today, many people are realizing that they can have quality products for less money using the do-it-yourself approach. For example, the Heath Company in Benton Harbor, Michigan has been a recognized leader in the electronics industry for many years. They offer nothing but kits to build stereos, computers, amateur radio equipment, etc. All of the components are included. The only thing the owner has to do is assemble them. This is where the instruction booklet can make or break a business of this type. RotorWay has excelled in the how-to-put-it-together category. They offer more than an instruction book. This facet of ownership will be further discussed.

The federal government has an approved program for the ownership of homebuilt aircraft. This is called the Amateur Built category, and under this program, the owner may save up to 75% on the cost of the home built aircraft. Savings abound for those putting together the Scorpion 133. First, there is the recognized savings in building it yourself, but there are additional savings which apply only to a do-it-yourself *aircraft project*. The high cost of federal certification, which adds thousands of dollars to a production line model, is avoided. Buying direct from the factory eliminates the middleman profit. There are tremendous savings on maintenance for aircraft in this category, as the FAA allows the owner to perform all of his or her own maintenance. Home constructed aircraft are placarded with the word "Experimental." This means that they are licensed under the FAA's Experimental category. It is safe to say that RotorWay's success in marketing this product indicates the willingness of many pilots to construct their own aircraft in order to take advantage of these wavings.

With the Scorpion 133, it isn't the rotor system, the fuselage or controls that make it a success. Rather, it's RotorWay's overall concept which encompasses a complete program to insure owners' success. This starts with the See—Do—Photo Sequence instructions to show the owner how to construct the helicopter. Engineering assistance is available by phone or mail should any difficulties be encountered. Classroom training is provided for each owner and includes theory, maintenance, and construction techniques.

Probably the most essential part of the RotorWay program is basic flight training in the Scorpion helicopter at their factory location. Remarkably, this is *included in the purchase price* of the aircraft. Licensed pilots are taught how to safely and efficiently fly and maintain their helicopters. In the author's opinion, if even one of these program elements were excluded, RotorWay would not be the success it is today. This customer-tested program has made the Scorpion not only attractive but very practical. It allows you to have a commercial quality product for a fraction of the expected cost.

Taking a closer look at the various components and controls of the Scorpion 133 will allow the reader to get an idea of just what's involved in the construction of this aircraft. The cabin enclosure is constructed of lightweight fiberglass, has a large windscreen, and is aerodynamically designed for improved flight performance and stability. Directional movement is maintained with a cyclic control stick which tilts the rotor disc in whatever plane the pilot desires. The helicopter moves in the direction of the tilt and accelerates in proportion to the amount of tilt. The collective pitch stick adds or subtracts pitch equally from each rotor blade. Pitch is the angle at which the blade cuts through the air. This control allows the pilot to climb or descend as he or she chooses. As the collective pitch stick is moved up and down, a change in engine power is required. The twist-grip throttle is designed so that power is added or subtracted automatically.

The Scorpion Rotor system incorporates an elliptical hub plate designed to withstand stresses many times those encountered during physical operation. This two-blade semi-rigid teetering hub is covered by U.S. Patent.

As was previously mentioned, the power plant consists of a 133 cubic inch, 133 hp four-cylinder engine which powers the drive train. The elimination of a heavy, complex and costly transmission is achieved through use of an ingenious two-stage reduction system. The first stage is a V-belt drive which allows for controlled rotor blade slippage during start-up and absorbs engine torsional vibration during operation. The second stage is a chain drive which allows for high torque transfer to the rotor shaft with a minimum loss of efficiency.

A simple system of three belts in tandem drives the Scorpion tail rotor. The V-belt system absorbs the vibrations of the rotor, eliminates the need for a tail rotor gear box, and offers a very significant cost savings over other designs. The tail rotor features a wraparound aluminium skin fastened to a steel bar. The simplicity and reliability of this unit is exceptional, and the extremely large rotor disc area results in whisper-quiet operation.

The airframe is constructed of aircraft steel using large diameter tubing for strength. Maximum rigidity and safety is offered through a design composed of multiple triangulated sections of this material.

RotorWay estimates the hourly direction operating cost of the Scorpion 133 to be $9.75 per hour. This would compare to over $20.00 per hour for the least expensive commercial helicopter, which would cost in excess of $80,000. Table 9-1 shows a performance chart for the Scorpion 133 which has a maximum range of 120 miles.

As has already been noted, the Scorpion 133 helicopter is a compact source of transportation. Figure 9-3 shows a three-view drawing stating the various dimensions of this aircraft. Maximum length is less than 30 feet, so it is quite conceivable that this 1,200 pound aircraft could be stored in a garage or farm building.

FLYING A HELICOPTER

Unlike conventional aircraft, a helicopter does not require thousands of feet of runway on which to land or take off. It is capable of performing these maneuvers in any area which is large enough to allow for the swing of its rotor blades. This capability provides an immeasurable increase in freedom of operation and allows the helicopter to be operated in and out of areas which are completely inaccessible by airplane. RotorWay notes that the helicopter is truly a sport flying machine because the fun of being able to make it an extension of the pilot's thought is both a challenging and rewarding experience. The pilot can practice and refine maneuvers of his own choosing, thus creating his own style as proficiency increases.

In order to fully understand the operation of any helicopter, it is first necessary to comprehend the control functions. Figure 9-4 shows the various controls relevant to the Scorpion 133. As was previously mentioned, the cyclic control determines direction, while a collective control adds or subtracts lift. The foot pedals control direction of rotation, either right or left, in a hover or in a right or left bank while in forward flight. Additionally, there is a throttle control which is normally a twist-grip affixed to the end of the collective control. In RotorWay helicopters, as in other helicopters the throttle is coordinated so that as pitch is added to the main blade, the additional power required is automatically fed into the system.

Table 9-1. Performance Chart For The Scorpion 133 Helicopter (courtesy RotorWay Aircraft, Inc.).

	SCORPION	vs.	COMMERCIAL
Cruise	80-90 MPH		90-95 MPH
Rate of Climb	800 FPM		900 FPM
Range	120 miles		150 miles
Hover I.G.E.	5,500'		6000'
Gross Weight	1200 lbs.		2500 lbs.
Useful Load	420 lbs.		1000 lbs.
	(or 35% of gross weight)		(or 40% of gross weight)
Service Ceiling	10,000 feet**		12,000 feet
*D.O.C./Hr	$9.75		$22.50

*Direct Operator Cost/Hr
**Unturbocharged

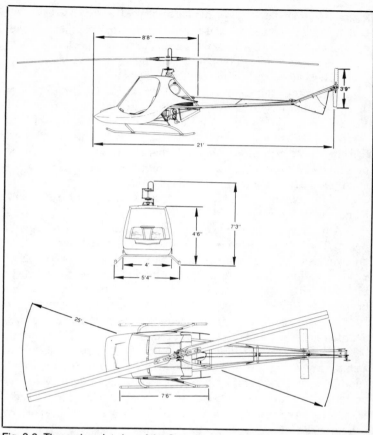

Fig. 9-3. Three-view drawing of the Scorpion 133 helicopter giving dimensions (courtesy RotorWay Aircraft, Inc.).

Now, what's it like to learn to fly a helicopter? Maneuvers begin with learning the basic hover. In order to do this, enough lift must be provided in the rotor system to overcome gravity and, at the same time, carefully balance the craft in order to maintain a flight position over one spot on the ground. Additionally, the pilot must counteract the torque which the engine puts into the main rotor drive shaft. This is done by feeding in the appropriate amount of foot pedal control to maintain a desired heading.

RotorWay notes that a student's first attempt at controlling a helicopter in a hover usually results in considerable entertainment for spectators. Control movements must not only be smooth and precise; they must be small. In other words, a light touch on the controls is mandatory. The novice pilot always seems to overcontrol, making the ship gyrate in an awkwardly funny manner. Most of the helicopter pilots who make up this group of spectators laugh because they can remember going through the same thing themselves in the early hours of their training program.

To protect the fledgling pilot from himself during his first attempt at learning to hover, RotorWay provides a Scorpion Sky Center Training Program. A factory-trained FAA Certified Flight Instructor helps the student learn the controls in a factory aircraft. This training in a properly rigged craft is an invaluable aid when the new pilot begins checking out and operating his own helicopter. He soon learns to separate his left hand from his right hand and to control each independently. This causes the ship to respond in a manner of his own choice.

After mastering the hover, ground taxiing maneuvers will begin. The ship is moved off its spot either forward, rearward, or sideways slowly at first and then with increasing speed. The basic ground taxiing maneuvers are performed at speeds from five to eight mph. In addition, 90, 180, and 360 degree turns on a spot will be practiced in both directions. What is commonly known as a "square pattern" (Fig. 9-5) maneuver will be practiced to further sharpen the student pilot's ground taxiing technique. The ship will be held in a constant heading and moved in the form of a square or as a ship is moved around the square, the nose may be rotated facing outside on each side of the square. The square pattern may also be performed by having the nose of the ship face into the square and a 90 degree turn made at each corner of the square while the pattern is being practiced.

The most difficult condition under which the helicopter, as a mechanism, is called upon to perform is the *hover*. As the helicopter begins to move forward with increasing speed, it moves off its ground cushion and enters what is known as *translational lift* (Fig. 9-6). In translational flight, there is an additional amount of lift gained by the rotor system as the ship accelerates from 15 mph to 45 mph. During this translational phase portion of flight, the pilot will find that it is not necessary to apply as much power or as much anti-torque in order to maintain his heading or altitude. Translational flight maneuvers are performed in slow flight to acquaint the pilot with this additional lift.

After having learned to hover the helicopter acceptably and after gaining experience in understanding translational flight, the pilot is ready to begin normal climbout (Fig. 9-7) and approach procedures. Any helicopter is capable of vertical takeoff and also capable of climbing vertically out of any spot just big enough to swing its rotor blades. Should power be lost, however, during a vertical climbout, it might be difficult to land the ship without damage. Therefore, a normal climbout consists of pulling the ship into a standard three or four foot hover and beginning forward flight through translational flight until a speed of 35 to 50 mph has been achieved. As soon as this speed has been achieved, a climb to altitude begins.

The normal approach (Fig. 9-8) is basically just the same as normal climbout, but in reverse. The pilot reduces his collective pitch, causing the ship to descend. A speed somewhere in the neighborhood of 50 mph is maintained on approach. Prior to arriving at the intended landing spot, the pilot will flare the ship, slowing whatever amount of forward speed is remaining and at the same time pulling into a hover over his intended landing site.

The helicopter operates in a fluid medium. Therefore, a factor known as *density altitude* must be taken into consideration. High altitude or very thin air along with high temperatures can effectively increase the altitude above ground at which the aircraft is desired to be flown. Before takeoff the pilot must make a simple calculation to determine what his density altitude is, regardless of the elevation of his departure. The helicopter is very adaptable to taking off at higher elevations due to the fact that it can make a run along the ground to gain translational lift even though the ship may not be able to hover prior to initiating a normal climbout. This

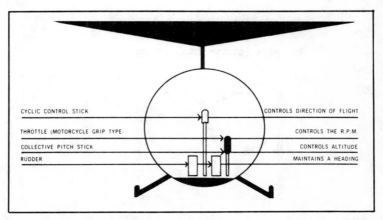

Fig. 9-4. Various controls relevant to the Scorpion 133 helicopter (courtesy RotorWay Aircraft, Inc.).

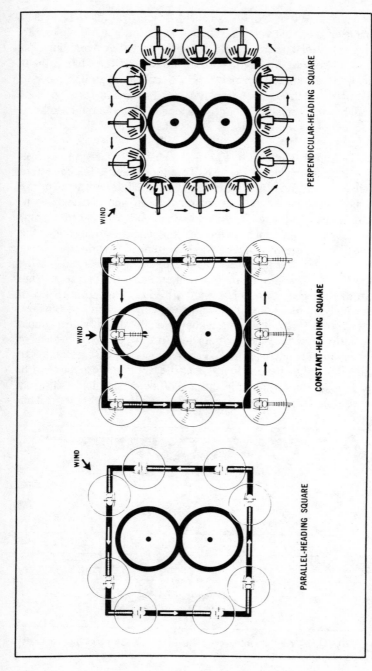

Fig. 9-5. Square pattern maneuver (courtesy RotorWay Aircraft, Inc.).

PERPENDICULAR-HEADING SQUARE

CONSTANT-HEADING SQUARE

PARALLEL-HEADING SQUARE

WIND

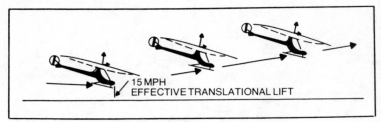

Fig. 9-6. Translational-lift (courtesy RotorWay Aircraft, Inc.).

procedure is known as the *high altitude takeoff* (Fig. 9-9). In this case, full power is applied to the craft and enough collective pitch is added in order to lift the ship so that forward motion may begin. As soon as translational lift is achieved, a slight back pressure on the cyclic control will allow the ship to climb and the pilot may depart the area under perfect control. The high altitude takeoff may be practiced at a lower altitude by merely limiting the amount of collective pitch, thus pretending that the maximum power available is already being applied.

The helicopter is a coordination machine and there are many precision maneuvers which may be made with the ship that are not absolutely necessary to just take off and land. One of these maneuvers is the *quick stop* (Fig. 9-10). Learning the quick stop requires that the helicopter pilot develop a precise coordination of application of power, altitude of craft and heading. The quick stop may be defined just as simply as it sounds. It is merely a matter of being able to stop the ship at whatever forward speed the pilot chooses without gaining or losing a significant amount of altitude. The quick stop is very useful in the sense that it helps the pilot to develop the coordination which he will need later in learning his power-off of autorotational procedures.

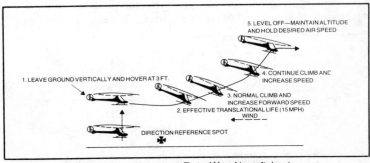

Fig. 9-7. Climbout procedure (courtesy RotorWay Aircraft, Inc.).

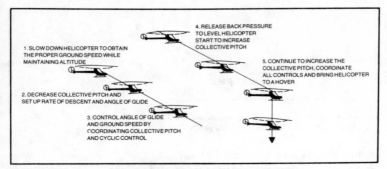

Fig. 9-8. Approach procedure (courtesy RotorWay Aircraft, Inc.).

SAFETY CONCEPTS OF THE HELICOPTER

Many persons not familiar with helicopters often express concern over pilot and passenger safety should an engine failure occur. Most persons know that an airplane has the ability to glide for a distance after the engine has stopped but feel that a helicopter would plunge to the ground should the same situation develop.

Actually, the helicopter is probably a safer aircraft than the airplane when both are subjected to engine failure. While it's true an airplane will glide, it must maintain a certain speed. If a fixed wing aircraft is slowed below its *stall* speed, it will just quit flying. The nose will drop suddenly and the plane will plunge unless enough airspeed is built up in the dive to allow it to maintain flight speed again. This does not occur in a helicopter. In fact, no power is needed in order for the helicopter to land in *autorotation*. This can be simply described as the speed of the air moving across the rotor in order to keep it turning after the engine has been shut down. This produces a windmilling effect; and, while the helicopter descends, it is a *controlled* descent which still offers the advantages of a zero forward speed landing. Many of us have witnessed maple seeds falling from a tree. These have a single leaf

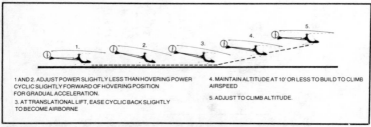

Fig. 9-9. High altitude takeoff (courtesy RotorWay Aircraft, Inc.).

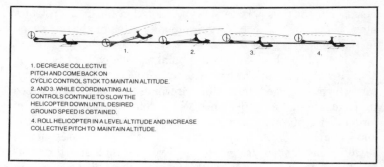

Fig. 9-10. Quick stop (courtesy RotorWay Aircraft, Inc.).

vein attached to the pod which causes them to spin as they leave the tree. As the seed first begins to fall, the speed of descent causes the air to flow across the leafy prop. The fall is thus slowed. Many of the same principles apply to autorotation.

Practicing autorotation is a part of a helicopter pilot's flight maneuvers. When engine power is cut, the pilot goes into autorotation by lowering his collective to a point where no power need be applied to the main rotor shaft in order for the blades to maintain their proper rpm. As the ship descends to the ground, the pilot flares the helicopter to slow to the desired ground speed and to dissipate all forward speed just prior to leveling and touching down. Figure 9-11 shows this procedure.

RotorWay stresses that the autorotational maneuver is practiced over and over by the pilot during their training program. Eventually, he or she will feel as comfortable in autorotation as in making a precision normal approach. The coordination maneuver described previously as the quick stop greatly assists the pilot in

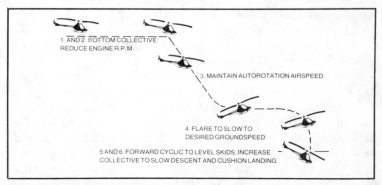

Fig. 9-11. Autorotation maneuver (courtesy RotorWay Aircraft, Inc.)

performing the final portion of his autorotational maneuver. Quick stops should be mastered before the pilot attempts his power off learning phase.

Most of our discussion to this point has involved the Scorpion 133. However, RotorWay has recently introduced another helicopter which is based upon the Scorpion but offers improved performance and an appearance which conforms more to that of larger helicopters. Named the RotorWay Exec, this aircraft is shown in Fig. 9-12. It features a fully enclosed, streamlined, teardrop fuselage which gives the Exec its high speed performance. The use of a water-cooled engine makes this possible. An air-cooled powerplant in a buried installation has never proven very effective, and RotorWay notes that with water cooling, the radiator can be positioned anywhere in the slipstream for positive cooling.

The Exec airframe features a combination of space frame and monocoque construction. An extremely light but rigid tube structure is used to provide hard points to which the rotor mast, powerplant, and landing gear are attached. The tail boom is a stressed-skin conical structure which is pop-riveted together with four simple castings and longitudinal stringers.

A totally new, ultra-simple cyclic control system is employed in this helicopter. Dual push-pull cables on the lateral and fore and aft axis eliminate all the bell cranks and push-pull rods that are normally used. Cyclic rigging is so easy that the dual load path provides a fail-safe design.

When the fiberglass fuselage panels pop out of the molds at RotorWay, that's all there is to it. No additional glass work has to be done. The joggles and lap joints are in the mold itself. Construction involves the installation of nut plates for the various attachments. Sanding and painting then takes place.

The RotorWay Exec is available with a new higher horsepower engine than its older sister. Displacement of its 162 cubic inches cranks out 145 horsepower, so owners of this bird will be able to operate normally aspirated in mountainous areas heretofore considered exclusive territory of turbine engine helicopters.

Doors are standard equipment, and even though the Exec is fully enclosed, it weighs less when empty than the Scorpion 133. This savings has been achieved through careful frame design and by a significant weight reduction in the control system. New technology used throughout the Exec has not only resulted in the reduction of components, but those that are there now are

Fig. 9-12. RotorWay Exec helicopter (courtesy RotorWay Aircraft, Inc.).

multi-functional in design. Several new aluminum castings are employed which create a more functional and appealing aircraft from the construction and maintenance points of view.

Best of all, the basic well-proven dynamic components used in the Scorpion 133 drive train and rotor system are also used in the RotorWay Exec. The Exec's style is new, but the heart of this aircraft is not. It has been proven out in the Scorpion 133.

The RotorWay Exec, like the Scorpion, is a kit. It can be put together in a garage or other area which will protect it from the elements during the construction procedure. Figure 9-13 shows a three-view drawing of the Exec giving all dimensions.

Of note in the construction process is the fact that there is no attachment between the fiberglass shell and frame. The entire body is attached only to the seat bulkhead, which is bolted to the frame with four bolts. All inspection panels and engine cowlings are Dzus fastened for quick, easy removal. The remainder of the fiberglass skins and windscreen are fastened with Phillips head screws and nut plates. The tail cone attaches with easily accessible bolts, and the floor pan serves as the lower cabin bulkhead and also as the mounting surface for the instrument panel.

Total price of the RotorWay Exec is $21,892 (as of early 1981). Unlike most kits which offer a low base price to which is added many thousands of dollars when the necessary options are

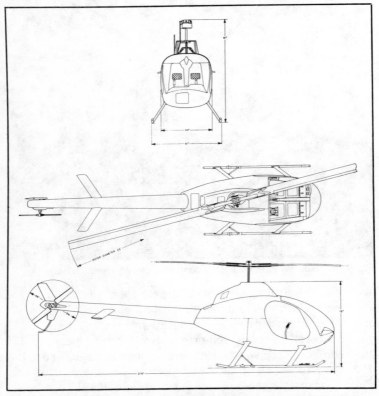

Fig. 9-13. Three-view drawing of the Exec helicopter giving dimensions (courtesy RotorWay Aircraft, Inc.).

included, this price is for a *complete*, flying helicopter kit. All the buyer has to do is assemble the parts and it can be flown away. The only optional equipment offered is dual controls, ground handling wheels, alternator/regulator, custom seat upholstery, and passenger seat belt and shoulder harnass. This latter option is certainly a necessity if you intend to carry a passenger. Cost for this last option is $90.00. Total cost of *all* optional equipment offered is only $671.00. Crating charges for the kit are about $300.00.

Now, just what will the Exec do? With its 145 horsepower water-cooled powerplant, maximum speed is 125 mph with a cruise speed of 105 mph. This betters the Scorpion 133 by over 15 mph. The Exec will climb at 1,200 fpm at sea level, will hover in ground effect at gross load at an altitude of 7,000 feet (this increases to 9,500 feet with a 60% load), and will hover out of ground effect at 4,000 feet. Its service ceiling is a minimum of 11,000 feet. Equipped useful load is 468 pounds. The payload with a full capacity of 14 gallons of fuel on board is 384 pounds. An optional fuel tank is available which will increase this capacity to a total of 19 gallons. With full optional fuel on board, the payload is 354 pounds.

Fuel flow at maximum cruise is about 8.5 gallons per hour. Range with maximum fuel at optimum cruise with one person on board is 234 miles in 2.2 hours. With two persons, 201 miles in 2.3 hours is the maximum range.

The available range with the Exec is about twice that of the Scorpion 133. As far as the author is concerned, this is probably the biggest selling point for this helicopter. Aesthetically speaking, the Rotorway Exec is a beautiful little helicopter. It has the appearance of helicopters costing in the half million dollar category and offers excellent range and performance. As RotorWay advertises, it offers turbine speed and styling on inexpensive piston power. For those who are mechanically inclined and have 700 or so hours available to put it together, the Exec is an excellent buy. It is a lot more practical for many business purposes due to its extended range and performance characteristics. The homebuilder can take advantage of FAA regulations governing aircraft in the experimental category. By doing most of your own maintenance, a great deal of money can be saved.

SUMMARY

The personal helicopter is not a thing of the future. It is here *now*. The RotorWay models were presented in this chapter to show the practicality of going the homebuilt route in order to save money. For the price of a well-equipped Lincoln Continental or Cadillac Seville, anyone can purchase all of the components for his or her own personal helicopter.

All that's required to be licensed to pilot an aircraft which you have built is a standard private pilot's certificate. No special license certification is necessary, as would be the case if you purchased a commercially built helicopter which is licensed in a different category.

While it is certainly a fact that the personal helicopter is economical and practical for a wide variety of uses, the exotic factor is an inpetus for many purchases. There is something very unique about owning your own means of air transportation, especially when it is an aircraft which you put together, test, fly and then store away for the night in your garage, just like you do with your automobile.

Chapter 10

Alternate Aircraft

Alternate aircraft have been mentioned previously in this book and offer another means of air transportation. The modern sailplane offers many improvements over the gliders of earlier years, just as the modern airplane is a much refined machine compared to those which were prevalent in the early part of this century. There is far more interest in piloting powered aircraft than gliders, but both factions are firmly dedicated to their pursuits.

Early sailplanes were designed to reduce aircraft weight to an absolute minimum, since simply remaining airborne was the main objective of the pilot. This is still, of course, a major concern today, but speed, distance, and performance are also prime considerations. Practical versatility is another factor which has influenced modern sailplane design, and most of these aircraft are fitted with detachable wings which enable the entire assembly to be transported by trailer. Now, the modern soaring enthusiast can keep his sailplane in a medium-sized garage and haul it to the airport behind his family sedan.

A trailered glider is shown in Fig. 10-1. While resembling an airplane in many ways, there are many differences as well. The length of the wing is probably the striking feature of sailplane design and is meant to provide as much lift as possible. These craft possess excellent aerodynamic characteristics and allow the pilot to take full advantage of favorable air currents.

Sailplanes of the past were marginally equipped regarding flight instrumentation. Today, the instrument system has been greatly expanded and includes the conventional indicators of altitude, airspeed, climb ar descent rate, etc. The rate-of-climb instrument is the one gli : pilots depend upon most, as it tells them whether the aircraft is ascending or descending. This device differs from the type used in powered aircraft. These tend to respond more slowly and are insensitive to small changes in altitude. The standard rate-of-climb instrument indicator used in the sailplane is called a *variometer*. It offers the reaction speed and sensitivity required for this type of operation.

LAUNCHING A SAILPLANE

In olden days, sailplanes were often launched from sloping runways which began at the top of a high hill or mountain and descended down the steep sides. Some were even launched from the edge of cliffs in much the same fashion that the launching of hang gliders is handled today. This, obviously, would severely limit sailplane activity, and several different methods which offer a great deal more practicality are in use today. The most commonly used towing method in modern times is an airplane-assisted ride in which a cable is attached to the nose of the glider and to the aft end of the airplane. The requirements for the towplane are an FAA approved towhook for attaching the towline and sufficient power to get a 700-pound sailplane to altitude. The plane must climb at a slow speed of less than 90 mph, so a high horsepower-to-weight ratio is necessary. The approved towhook is designed to enable the airplane pilot to remotely release his end of the towline in an emergency. The sailplane pilot has a similar release mechanism which is controlled from his craft. When the sailplane has reached altitude, its pilot releases the towline and immediately banks to rid itself of the weight turbulence created by the towplane. The airplane pilot will then often release the towline over the air field, allowing it to drop to the ground or, in some instances, he may elect to land with the towline still attached.

The auto-tow is another method which is occasionally used, especially from remote grassy fields. An automobile is used to tow the glider to launch speed on this field or runway, but usually a lot of runway length is required. Wind conditions must be ideal for this type of launch, meaning that velocities should be rather high. The main disadvantage of this method is that the glider must be released while in still close proximity to the ground. From this point on, the pilot must depend upon his skill and favorable winds to keep him aloft and to allow for a gain in altitude.

Fig. 10-1. A glider or sailplane resembles a long-winged conventional airplane but contains no powerplant.

Another launching method which is more popular in foreign countries than here in the United States is to use a power winch to rapidly accelerate the cable and its attached glider. The sailplane is connected to a long towline which is rapidly wound up by winch, normally located at the opposite end of the runway. This can be likened in many ways to the launching of aircraft from large carriers at sea. The sailplane is not brought up to speed gradually but is literally yanked down the runway. This sudden increase in speed causes the sailplane to enter a very steep rate of climb with the pilot leveling off as he passes over the winch. At this point, the sailplane pilot releases the cable by means of his towhook control. Sometimes, a small parachute is activated by this release which allows this winch to continue to wind in the cable without it becoming hopelessly entangled.

A winch launching is very inexpensive but does involve many problems. One of these is similar to the one encountered in the previously discussed auto-launch procedure, in that the aircraft is released while still very close to the ground. One advantage when compared to an auto-tow is that the winch launch can be used at limited runway facilities because of the almost immediate acceleration involved. This system might be used at a short field where the auto-tow could not even be attempted.

After the sailplane has been released from its cable, regardless of the launching method, it is in free flight and is handled in much the same manner as a powered airplane. Sailplane controls are usually not as crisp or responsive as are the controls of its powered counterparts because of the generally larger control surface areas. The pilot is intimately aware of the weather conditions and air currents he seeks and, after launch, will be looking for an immediate lifting current to enable him to gain altitude.

In order to seek out desirable air currents, the pilot will closely monitor his variometer and will also look for ground features which tend to create updrafts. For example, a slope or ridge may serve as a good indication because when wind strikes these obstacles, it is forced upward. This type of lift is the simplest to identify, and beginning as well as experienced sailplane pilots take advantage of it whenever possible.

The most frequently used lift in sailplaning is by means of *thermals*. This can be thought of as a large column of air which rises from the earth due to heating effects. Hot air balloons work on the same principle, although the thermals are generated within the craft itself. Hot air rises and so does the balloon. The same principle applies when the sailplane "rides a thermal."

There are various ways to recognize the areas where thermals are most likely to exist. If the rising air is moist enough, the column will be marked by a cumulus cloud if it rises to an altitude where condensation can take place. It is not necessary to have clouds in order to have a thermal. This is especially true when there is little moisture in the air. To find these types of conditions, the sailplane pilot must depend heavily upon his variometer. He will also be watching any flying birds he encounters, especially buzzards, who are probably the most expert glider pilots in the business.

There are many other forms of air currents which will provide lift for the sailplane pilot. Indeed, entire texts have been written on this subject alone. The beginning sailplane enthusiast is taught from the start to become initimately involved with weather conditions and air current effects. The powered aircraft pilot considers weather and air currents, generally, as factors to be contended with. The sailplane pilot looks upon these same conditions as the power source for his craft.

LANDING A SAILPLANE

Unlike a powered aircraft which can easily go around and try again if a landing pattern is botched up, the sailplane pilot *must* do it right the *first time*. Landing a sailplane, however, is not nearly as difficult as bringing in most powered aircraft, as the approach speeds are much slower and excellent glide path control is provided by the basic sailplane design. The approach to the airport is handled in the same manner as when flying powered aircraft, although the beginning of this approach will probably occur in much closer proximity to the airfield to be certain of reaching it. From this point on, the sailplane pilot keeps a close check on approach speed and rate of descent. This latter figure must be judged to bring the aircraft within close proximity of the runway shortly after crossing the threshold. Most of us have seen glider touchdowns on television, and they seem to come floating in very slowly and effortlessly; however, the pilot has worked very hard to make it look this effortless, and many powered aircraft pilots are amazed at the precision with which these touchdowns are made.

Sailplaning has become a very popular sport in the United States. This has been brought about by the many improvements in glider design and by the formation of sailplane clubs in many areas. The FAA licensing requirements are not as stringent as those placed on pilots of powered aircraft, so progression from student to solo is usually quicker and less costly. Sailplanes tend to be less expensive than powered aircraft, but they are not cheap. However, many used aircraft may be purchased at substantial savings. Some people feel that glider pilots are simply training to move up to powered aircraft. This is generally not true, as many sailplane pilots became so after many hours of powered flight. Sailplaning enthusiasts are often considered to be the purists in the flying fraternity, and it's been said that sailplane pilots and powered aircraft pilots do not often get along nor see eye to eye. The author has never witnessed any out-and-out animosity between the two groups, but often their ideas and viewpoints about man's place in the sky do differ.

HOT AIR BALLOONS

Though developed as one of the first means of flight, the popularity of the hot air balloon has really come into its own within the last twenty years. Today, more and more individuals are taking up ballooning, clubs have been formed, and massive ballooning events are held in almost every area of the country. Recently, a hot air balloon was piloted across the Atlantic, landing in France. Attempts are now being made to make an around-the-world voyage in this type of craft, paralleling Jules Verne's story *Around the World in Eighty Days*. Modern balloonists anticipate the circumnavigation in far less time, however.

The hot air balloon shown in Fig. 10-2 is basically a large bag which is filled with heated air and to which is attached a partially enclosed "basket" in which pilot and passengers are carried aloft. The bag is not fully enclosed by any means, as a valve is located at the topmost portion (Fig. 10-3). This is actually a hole through which the air can be allowed to escape. This opening is controlled by a valve line which is channeled down through the center of the balloon. The bottom portion of the balloon is called the *neck* and is held constantly open to allow for heated air to rise into the balloon compartment. The air is heated while in flight by means of a gas burner which shoots a jet of flame upward toward the neck opening. This causes the heated air to be collected in the balloon. When a balloonist desires additional lift, the gas burner is activated. When a reduction in altitude is needed, the top valve is opened more fully to release a certain quantity of air.

Covering the thin, non-porous envelope which makes the balloon is a series of cables or even a netting arrangement which begins at the top valve opening and extends down the sides of the balloon. These cables are symmetrically positioned about the balloon to enable the basket or "car" to be attached. This is where the pilot and passengers are carried, and it must be attached in such a manner as to allow the entire balloon to take the stress evenly.

Flight instruments used for balloon operation are generally very basic when compared to those systems installed in powered

Fig. 10-2. A hot air balloon consists of a large, non-porous bag which is filled with heated air (courtesy of the *Warren Sentinel*).

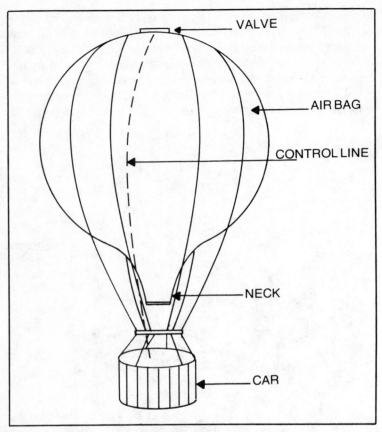

VALVE

AIR BAG

CONTROL LINE

NECK

CAR

Fig. 10-3. The various parts of a hot air balloon.

aircraft. A compass, sensitive rate-of-climb indicator, and a few maneuvering controls normally form the complement. You don't actually maneuver a balloon in the same manner as you do a glider or airplane. The latter ride *on* or *through* the air, while the balloon, more or less, becomes a *part* of it. The balloon goes where the air goes. The only maneuverability which can be had is in the vertical direction. This is controlled by the amount of lift presented by the balloon. A balloon pilot depends heavily upon weather forecasts and attempts to get some idea of what air currents are doing at various altitudes. He also depends upon geographical formations which affect air currents to maintain or change his direction of flight. For example, if an easterly course is desired, the balloonist will allow his craft to ascend to the altitude where air currents tend to take an easterly course. When he desires to move in the opposite direction, he may ascend to a higher altitude or descend in order to ride the current which is going his way.

A balloon pilot really has no sense of air currents, in that he doesn't really feel the air against his body. The balloon becomes a part of the wind and presents little resistance to its flow. This is different from an airplane which flies through the air, often traveling in opposition to prevailing air currents.

Balloons are less expensive than airplanes. But like everything else involved with flying, they are not cheap either. A typical hot air balloon will often cost ten, fifteen, or even twenty thousand dollars. Some will even greatly exceed these figures. A great deal of ground equipment is required in order to transport and initially inflate the hot air balloon. The collapsed balloon is painstakingly positioned in an open field, and huge fans blow cool air through its opening to begin the inflation process. Once the material begins to open, gas heat blowers begin to fill the bag with heated air. As the balloon slowly inflates, it begins to lift from the ground, and eventually this lift becomes adequate enough to cause the bag to assume an upright position. Several workers are required to stabilize the bag and to keep the gondola portion on the ground. Since the balloon is not yet flying, a great deal of work is required to keep the entire craft reasonably stationary. A hot air balloon is a most unwieldy device when on the ground. Small air currents at this point can cause the bag to drift back and forth and sometimes dump much of its hot air. But once liftoff is achieved, the hot air balloon becomes a most graceful craft and probably one of the most beautiful sights in all of aviation. Whereas airplane and glider pilots fly their craft, the hot air balloonist *is* flown. He goes where the air currents decide to take him, and while it is possible to maintain a form of maneuverability through altitude control, the balloonist is often at the mercy of the air currents.

This is where the ground crew is most instrumental. They attempt to track the flight of the balloon and to hopefully be on the scene at touchdown. Of course, the balloon takes an air route, whereas the ground crew must attempt to follow this route by means of conventional roads. Landing a hot air balloon is an experience unto itself and requires reaction procedures far in advance of those encountered in more conventional forms of flight. Generally speaking, the balloonist does not have immediate control of the craft, so a landing must be set up far in advance of the intended touchdown time and location. The pilot begins to decrease the craft's lift by allowing a specific amount of hot air to escape, and then during the last minutes before touchdown most of the lift is "dumped." Ideally, the balloon will land in almost still air while making no lateral progress. Practically speaking, however, there will always be some lateral movement, and the car will often be upset moments after touchdown.

Ballooning is exciting, but it's also a very safe (if not highly practical) means of transportation. Ballooning should be thought of as sport flying and is rarely used for pure transportation purposes. However, a logging company recently used an unmanned hot air balloon tethered by means of long steel cables to transport logs from the top of a nearly inaccessible mountain to its base. Winches were installed at the mountain peak and at the base, and the balloon was pulled from one site to another by using the connecting cables. At the top of the mountain, huge logs were attached to the bottom of the balloon by means of another cable and then the winch at the base was activated. When the balloon reached the bottom of the mountain, a mechanical switch released the logs and the balloon was hauled back to the top again. This was a very efficient means of logging and saved the company many hundreds of thousands of dollars which would have been required to install a road and to maintain vehicular traffic between the two points.

Hot air balloons, again tethered to the ground, are sometimes used for observation purposes. These are often found at county fairs. Persons are allowed to be lofted to an altitude above the treeline and to gaze to their heart's content for a small fee. When the ride is over, the balloon is hoisted in again and another group enters the gondola. Sometimes, these balloons are sealed-bag devices which are designed only for ground control.

One of the most striking things about the hot air balloon is the ornamental and decorative designs which are painted upon the bag surfaces. It seems that each pilot has his own design and these are very reminiscent of the balloons of the 19th Century. Instrumentation and design have certainly improved since these days; but on the whole, hot air balloons remain much the same as they did hundreds of years ago, and it is a purist's pursuit. Licensing for this type of flying is far less complicated in requirements than is the case with powered aircraft. The beginning balloonist is usually restricted to tethered flight, allowing him or her to learn the proper control functions of this aircraft before being set free to ride the air currents.

SUMMARY

Sailplaning and hot air ballooning are forms of flight which have been with us for many hundreds of years. Modern aviation is based upon the advances made using these ancient aircraft. It may seem strange to note that as a specific field is advanced by modern science, there are always those individuals who seek to return to an earlier time when sophisticated designs and electronic instrumentation were not available. Such is the case with ballooning and, often, sailplanes. Those who pursue these forms of flight have, in some ways, entered time machines which take them back to the very earliest days when man took to the air. Fortunately, all of the modern advances have not been done away with, and those that remain multiply the safety factor by many hundreds of times. It is this mixture, the old and the new, which makes these alternate forms of flight so attractive today.

Chapter 11

Flying Fun

Throughout this text, the technical aspects of flying have been discussed in order to acquaint the reader with much of what is involved in obtaining a license and obtaining an airplane to fly. The many advantages air travel offers over more conventional means have also been touched upon, but to many, flying offers a feeling of freedom which is unavailable when traveling on the ground. Ask any pilot why he flies and he or she will probably tell you, "Because it's fun."

True enjoyment cannot be bought. An investment of time, practice, and devotion is required in order to fully enjoy almost any pursuit we humans decide to tackle. And so it is with flying. Aside from the monetary expenditure, a great outpouring of work has been required to achieve the goal of a private license.

As is the case with many endeavors, once licensed, the new pilot may think *"Now* what do I do? " The answer is simple. You take full advantage of that license and enjoy it to the extent which is practical for you.

After many hours of solo flying as a student pilot, the new holder of a private pilot's license will normally set as his first goal the flying of a friend or loved one through the skies of the nearby airport. The accomplishment of this goal is further enhanced by the pleasure he sees in the eyes of his or her passengers as he acquaints them with the exotic medium in which they travel. There is no real purpose to these first flights other than to enjoy the freedom which has been hard won.

After awhile, these excursions become fewer and fewer and the pilot will seek to expand the enjoyment factor by adding variety to this mode of travel. The author can still remember calling a girlfriend in a distant city, asking her to have coffee with him at the airport cafeteria near her home. Some of the words in that sentence are vividly recalled even today, such as, "I'm doing some travel up your way this afternoon and plan to land at the municipal airport around 2:30. How about meeting me there and we can have a cup of coffee before I take off for home?" The awe and excitement she expressed by her quick, positive reply was an immediate indication to me of the position she, like most people, automatically put pilots into. My nonchalance in making the invitation and discussing the flight was a successful effort in hiding my excitement over the prospect of this trip.

After having given this friend the impression that I was simply going to routinely hop into the plane and fly over in the same manner as if I were coming in an automobile, I plotted my course, taking into account the predicted wind factor, and methodically performed the walk-around inspection on the Cessna 150 that I was renting. While the flight was not a difficult one, I had decided that I would navigate by flying a pre-planned course rather than to simply follow the highway between my city and hers.

It was a beautiful May afternoon with very little wind and excellent visibility. No clouds could be seen in the sky. Lifting off from my home airport. I quickly climbed to 2,500 feet, hit the start of my plotted course, and was delighted that my flight perfectly coincided with all ground checkpoints along the way.

After a pleasant flight of less than a half hour, I spotted the municipal airport directly ahead. I scoffed at the earth-bound automobiles below, each of them weaving to and fro with the others in an attempt to make the best time in the heavy Saturday traffic. Even those automobiles on the interstate to my left whose course I paralleled were being left hopelessly behind by the 100 mph speed of my aircraft.

Although the municipal airport was uncontrolled, I radioed my intentions to land and asked for their active runway. No reply came back, which meant the FBO was probably out fueling an aircraft. Taking safety into account, I decided to wait for a response by overflying the airport by a mile or so, turned 180 degrees, and set up an approach to the runway which the windsock indicated would be best to use. Temporarily thinking about the friend who would be waiting for me on the ground, I was not paying close attention to my compass when I effected my 180 degree turn. Suddenly, I realized the airport was *not* where it should be. I re-checked my compass and found that I was about 10 degrees off course and a sudden wind had probably pushed me a bit to the east of my destination. I corrected course and calmly searched for my goal. *It just wasn't there*. As a matter of fact, I could no longer see the interstate highway which should have been plainly visible to my right. A bit of ground haze was building up due to the heat of the day which made discernment of close ground details a bit difficult. The situation was becoming embarrassing.

After fifteen minutes of searching, I decided that I didn't know where I was and had better give up and follow the mountains to my left back to my home airport. I could have radioed the municipal airport and identified some ground points in order for them to give me a heading, but the airport unicom had a speaker in the cafeteria where my friend would most certainly be waiting by this time. I had plenty of fuel, was fully confident of finding my way back home (because of the mountain range), and would not suffer the indignity of letting the friend whom I had impressed so much on the phone know that I was lost. I envisioned a phone explanation to her of an emergency landing or some other such nonsense for the next fifteen minutes.

As I neared the halfway point home (based on the time I had been flying), I saw a rather large building about three miles to the west of my course and decided to fly over to see if it was anything I could recognize. Descending to 1,500 feet, I had the eerie experience of being stared at by a *full-size brontosarus*, a dinosaur which died out millions of years ago.

No, I hadn't entered the Twilight Zone; the animal I was staring back at was one of the attractions of "Prehistoric Park," a tourist attraction. I now knew where I was, quickly located the road which I was not going to use for navigation purposes on this trip and religiously followed it back to the municipal airport, my original destination. Upon spotting the airport again, I was immediately answered on the unicom, given the active runway, and made a beautiful landing. I was about twenty minutes late but explained it away to my anticipatory friend by citing several aviation terms with which she was totally unfamiliar.

The afternoon had gone all right after all; and after an hour of coffee, conversation, and several tall flying tales, I left for home wagging my wings impressively after leaving the pattern for my friend who watched from her car below.

The entire experience was mostly enjoyable and entirely educational. Even though I was a licensed pilot with many hours of flight time under my belt, there were still many mistakes that could and would be made and much more to learn. I feel this way even today.

This true story typifies flying for me. It is always interesting, very much fun, and demanding. This is not to say that you can't relax when you are flying, for you certainly can. It does demonstrate, however, that you must earn your fun by putting forth the proper concentration that is required. All pilots get lost from time to time. This is a part of flying, but with a little common sense, the right path is found. This and a million other aspects are all a part of the pursuit.

FLYING VACATIONS

Flying vacations are the ultimate in fun for the average private pilot. There are many areas which are within easy reach by airplane which cannot be considered as part of the itinerary for a weekend vacation when traveling by automobile. For those of us on the East Coast, a flying trip to the Bahamas is a dream which is often realized. The first leg of the journey is normally between the home airport and the southern tip of Florida. This leg may be traveled in one or several days, depending upon the plans of the pilot, the distance involved, and the type of plane being flown.

Once in Florida, all legalities are squared away for the trip across the "pond." The flight from the mainland to the first Bahamiam island usually takes less than an hour. Most flying magazines will be filled with personal advertisements offering rental homes in the various islands. These can be had by the week for anywhere from $275 to about $600. All of these rentals have one thing in common. They are located close to airports. Some even have their own private runways. Extras often include scuba gear, bicycles, motorcycles, boats, etc.

Most people who fly to the Bahamas plan their itinerary far in advance. This allows them to see many of the islands without being confined to any one. "Island hopping" is what this is called and involves seeing as much of the Bahama chain as is comfortable and practical. The crystal-clear waters, delightful beaches and excellent flying conditions are sure to mean day after day of excitement and enjoyment.

The Bahamas are especially attractive to pilots because air transportation is looked upon as a *necessity*, as other than by boat the only way to get from one island to another is by light plane. And thousands of single-engine aircraft, as well as light twins, make the trip from the mainland each year. From a cost standpoint, it would probably be less expensive for one or two persons to take a commercial flight to and from one Bahamian island; but this completely precludes seeing many islands in this chain. It also takes away from the flexibility and freedom of the trip. Should four people travel to these islands by private plane, the overall costs factor is significantly reduced, as all expenses are shared equally. A private plane is almost as efficient with four on board as it is with one, so your actual flying time will produce more passenger miles per dollar.

Don't be lulled into thinking that you just pick up and go with a few days' planning for a trip of this nature. This would be a rather complex vacation, on which would require several months of planning in order to make reservations, check out the various legalities, properly outfit your plane for travel over the Atlantic Ocean, and to set a practical itinerary. Probably the most complex part of the journey as far as the actual flying is concerned would be from your home base to Florida. From here on out, things are not quite so complicated, although one must pay strict attention to navigation while in flight to the islands. Fortunately, there are radio beacons which make homing in on the desired island extremely easy. Besides, it is a short trip with much to see and will probably be thought of as one of the most interesting parts of the entire vacation.

For most of us, a flying trip to an exotic island is something to dream about, plan for—and probably never take. On a more practical note, there are many flying vacations or flying weekends that are far less complex, less expensive and highly enjoyable. Local airports abound throughout the United States, putting almost any area within easy reach by light plane. If you check the various brochures and travel folders, you will often see an indication of a local airport which serves a particular resort or attraction. Courtesy cars are sometimes provided by these vacation meccas, offering free transportation to and from the airport. Local airports also provide courtesy cars on occasion, so generally, getting from the landing site to your vacation spot is easily and inexpensively handled.

There is a growing trend among resort areas to operate their own airport facilities. Alternately, it will be advertised that a resort is looking for someone to build and operate an airport with financial backing being offered. This puts the airport operation into the hands of someone who has been working in this field, allowing him or her to run a business for personal profit. Of course, airport activities are coordinated with the resort, but the two are thought of as separate enterprises. Many resorts build their own airports and then lease the operation to an operator. It is up to this person to establish a profitable business for himself by selling fuel, maintenance, and so forth. Such an operation is of mutual benefit to both parties involved.

The reader may be thinking at this time that only very large resorts and attractions can afford to provide a runway and airport facilities for their visitors. By and large, the *opposite* is true. Most of the large vacation centers are already served by commercial airports, so private runways are usually a waste of money. Rather, it is the smaller family resorts that are taking advantage of this growing trend.

One excellent example of a vacation airport is located in Virginia only 25 miles from the author's home base. Luray Caverns in Luray, Virginia is a multi-faceted vacation center located in a rural community and off the beaten path. Luray Caverns has long been known for its magnificent underground formations and has often been called the most beautiful caverns in the world. This organization also operates a magnificent golf course, antique car showroom, a structure called the Singing Tower (Fig. 11-1) and an *airport*. This is a municipal airport at which Luray Caverns is the operator. The facility consists of a 3,500 foot landing strip, tie-down and fueling services, snack bar, and courtesy car to just about anywhere you want to go.

In talking with the public relations director of Luray Caverns, the author discovered that he was also a pilot who is very much enthralled with the airport operation and what it offers to air travelers. He reported that the golf course presently seems to be the largest direct attraction for vacationing pilots, but this is balanced by the caverns, antique auto showroom and all of the other recreation availabilities which are located in this area. The golf course abuts the airport facility, so it's a hop, skip and jump to the first hole. Flying vacations most often include the pilot's wife and children, so while Dad's beating his brains out on the ninth hole, non-golfing family members can be enjoying a caverns tour, lunch in any of the fine restaurants on the cavern grounds, and top it all off with a tour of the antique automobile showroom. If this trip is to be an overnighter, the caverns' personnel are happy to provide courtesy car service to one of their motels.

There are many other nearby attractions which include a Civil War Battlefield Park, canoeing on the Shenandoah River, or even

Fig. 11-1. The Singing Tower at Luray Caverns is one of the many sights a vacationing pilot will find a short distance from the airport (courtesy Luray Caverns, Luray, Virginia).

a trip by rental car down Skyline Drive whose entrance is less than a half hour from the airport.

In making the flight to Luray Caverns Airport, visitors coming from the north and south will often fly above the Shenandoah River. This forms a natural beacon, in serpentine fashion, to locate the airport which was built near water's edge. The approaches to this slightly elevated runway are excellent and, if the author's experience is any indication, you will be treated like royalty when you arrive.

Rates are very reasonable, but there is a lot to do and see, so a vacation of this type should not be crowded into a day or two if you plan to take advantage of all this area has to offer. Figure 11-2 shows the Luray Caverns Airport where we landed and tied down for a three-day trip. Our flight was anticipated, so we were greeted by the sight of the courtesy car waiting to take us to the caverns complex. Shown in Fig. 11-3, the building and grounds are awesome to say the least, but visitors are treated with genuine Southern Hospitality and are made to feel right at home. After enjoying lunch in one of the restaurants, it was decided that a tour

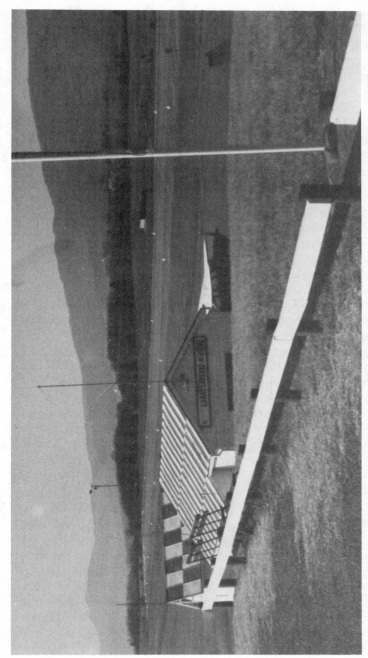

Fig. 11-2. The Luray Caverns Airport offers a 3,500 foot strip and magnificent view.

235

through the caverns would be in order. This takes about an hour and visitors should be certain to bring along a sweater or light jacket to ward off the chill that a constant temperature in the mid fifties can bring on. Figure 11-4 shows just one of the many thousands of views we had on this hour tour.

After exiting the cave, the next stop on our mini-itinerary was the antique car showroom which is equally as awesome as the caverns. We jokingly asked the public relations director if he intended to establish an antique aircraft museum, to which he replied, "I'll think about it."

The following day was tee-off time at the beautiful golf course. Shown in Fig. 11-5, this 18-hole "Siren" has lured many to certain doom in the form of scores greatly exceeding 100. It is as challenging as it is beautiful, providing hours of serious competition for those who take the game seriously.

In order to forget about the previous day's golf score, the final morning of our vacation was spent on the Shenandoah National Park and Skyline Drive. This winding highway through the heart of the Blue Ridge Mountains is guaranteed to make a pilot feel airborne again with the spectacular views of the entire valley from altitudes approaching 4,000 feet. Figure 11-6 provides a description of this panorama which cannot be effectively put into words.

Near day's end, all of our vacation gear was hauled back to the airport, stashed in the baggage compartment of the Cessna 172, and we were soon headed back to home base. To wax poetic, the setting sun, offering its waning light to be reflected off the Shenandoah River, formed a corollary to our vacation which was only now coming to an end. But as sure as Sol would return again on the 'morrow, we would also be returning at some future date to enjoy the wonders we had beheld.

FLY-IN RESORTS

A fly-in resort offers many variations for recreation opportunities, and a check of the travel folders will likely uncover quite a few which lie within easy reach of your home base. One such example in the author's home state of Virginia is Bryce Resort in Bayse, which is definitely off the beaten path. Bryce Resort is a relatively new vacation area which is nestled in a miniature valley and surrounded by beautiful mountains. Bryce offers year-round recreation with an eighteen hole golf course, tennis courts, excellent skiing area with lifts, and a 2,500 foot paved runway. The airport even offers flying lessons for guests and residents. The

Fig. 11-3. Southern hospitality is exuded by the building and grounds of Luray Caverns and is a favorite of pilots who utilize the Luray Caverns Airport.

Fig. 11-4. The interior of Luray Caverns offers sights as magnificent as the panoramic view from the airport (courtesy Luray Caverns, Luray, Virginia).

approaches to this runway are a bit tricky upon a first landing due to the mountainous surroundings, but access here is certainly within the reach of any private pilot. Of interest to pilots is the large twin-engine Lockheed which is owned by Pete Bryce, the millionaire developer and pilot who started the whole thing. To see him take off and land this large aircraft from the tiny runway is an experience one doesn't soon forget. Golfers on hole number 2 whose green lies at one end of the runway have been known to dive into sandpits when Pete's large taildragger comes over.

The author thinks of Bryce as being a family resort and although the setting is rustic, guests are immediately impressed

Fig.11-5. Vacationing pilots often take time out to play a round of golf on the eighteen hole course which abuts the airport (courtesy Luray Caverns, Luray, Virginia).

239

with the plushness of their accommodations. Visitors to Bryce Resort have the option of staying in a condominium, some of which will sleep eight. All are equipped with kitchenettes, stone fireplaces, and televisions. Alternately, a townhouse may be chosen which abuts the golf course and offers comfortable quarters on two floors. For the height of luxury, groups may elect to rent an entire chalet which sleeps many and provides a spectacular view of the surroundings. Reservations should be placed well in advance.

One of the finest features of this resort is an excellent restaurant with a huge raftered ceiling and equally large stone fireplace, in which an adult could easily stand upright. Diners may comfortably consume a gourmet meal while viewing skiers cascading down the slopes. This sight can be enjoyed year round, as even in the summer, grass skiers abound. Many grass skiing championships are held at Bryce Resort. Many pilots within Bryce's realm of influence often take advantage of the restaurant by flying friends and family down for an evening meal, returning later that same night.

If you like to ski, as well as fly, Bryce offers some of the finest slopes in the area, with each being fed by chair lifts or T-bar. A large ski lodge can be relaxed in after your bout with the slopes and, as one would expect, there's a circular open hearth fireplace to thaw out frozen limbs. Ski instruction is provided either in groups or individually.

For those pilots and passengers who enjoy tennis, Bryce offers year-round facilities. The same courts are used in summer and winter, but during colder weather, they are covered with an air-inflated dome and heated.

Bryce's golf course comes complete with a pro shop, cart rentals and anything you want to buy which is related to this sport. One nine-hole course is located to one side of the main facility and parking lot, while the second nine is found on the opposite end. It will suffice to say that the fairways are fair and the rough is disastrous. This is a course for the golfer who can place the ball where he wants it. In the author's opinion, it's one of the most challenging courses he has ever played.

If you've found nothing of particular interest to you so far in this discussion, perhaps a sailboat ride on the magnificent lake located about two miles from the main facility will get your attention. You may even buy a fishing license and try your luck at angling for the lunker bass which are reputed to be found here. The Bryce Resort stables are located near the lake. Here, you can take

Fig. 11-6. The view of the valley from the Shenandoah National Park and Skyline Drive provides a pilot's-eye vantage point for earthbound travelers.

241

a grand tour of the mountains on horseback and with the aid of a guide.

Many people who visit Bryce Resort end up buying property at the resort or at Bryce Hill which abuts it. During the last visit the author made to this area, he was the guest of Pete Bryce, who is now developing a large solar home complex. Even the information office is affixed with solar panels. As Pete's guest, I was put up for the weekend in a veritable solar mansion sitting high atop one of the highest peaks around. Shown in Fig. 11-7, this "cabin" as Pete called it was outfitted with everything including a Jacuzzi and suana room. It was difficult to get back to normal life again after this weekend, which offered spectacular views like the one shown in Fig. 11-8.

In discussing Bryce Resort with its originator, Pete told me that he was amazed at the number of former military pilots who had bought property at Bryce Resort and ended up living there after retirement. The airport had a lot to do with their decision. Private pilots had also been influenced, as was evidenced in a discussion I had with a golfing partner I had met only the day of a tournament. He was an insurance executive from metropolitan area of Maryland who stated that he flew to Bryce every weekend, weather permitting, and would often come down for an evening during the week, flying back the next morning. He owned a chalet on the side of the mountain overlooking the golf course. He went on to affirm that if not for the airport, he couldn't even consider Bryce Resort, because it would be over four hours away by automobile. By plane, it took less than an hour and a half.

At this point, the reader may be getting concerned over the appearance of Bryce and other such flying resorts as being playgrounds for the wealthy. It would be incorrect to say they aren't, but it should be remembered that most resorts (Bryce included) exist on income from everyday persons. Prices for accommodations and meals, as well as for the recreational activities, would seem to reflect this. For every Mercedes Benz at the Bryce parking area, there are a dozen Volkswagons and Chevys. Likewise, there are many more inexpensive two and four-place used aircraft than there are brand-new turbocharged twins. Like most resorts, Bryce is designed to be fun, no matter what income bracket you happen to be in. It offers a quiet, relaxing time for those who seek this type of activity, or it can include a late night of partying and disco dancing at the Copper Kettle Club also located on the premises. If you're not independently wealthy, you

Fig. 11-7. This magnificent solar home was the author's headquarters for a Fly-In vacation at Bryce Resort.

Fig. 11-8. The rustic setting and spectacular view shown here are only a part of what the vacationing pilot can experience at Bryce Resort upon arrival.

might not buy property there, but you can sure have a good time on your flying vacation.

SUMMARY

This chapter has highlighted but a few of the many fun things that are suddenly opened to those persons who have put in the time and energy to obtain a pilot's license. Getting that license is not extremely difficult, but it's not easy either. By looking ahead to the rewards which can be had, almost anyone would have to agree that flying has the potential of giving you back much more than was originally put into it.

Maybe a flying trip to the Bahamas is completely out of the question right now, but weekend outings should be practical for almost anyone who has a pilot's license and can plan ahead by saving for such a trip. As you become more accustomed to the operation of aircraft and to the flying world in general, perhaps that exotic island won't be as unreachable as you originally thought.

In summing it all up, you really don't have to fly anywhere in particular or make any specific plans. There is something quietly entertaining about having the authority, the confidence, the ability and the freedom to climb into an airplane and just go.

Chapter 12

Flight Safety

Throughout this book, the author has made repeated references to safety in flying. This is what all aircraft, pilots and flying practices must be founded upon. Aviation pursuits are safe only because the manufacturers, pilots, and FAA Rules make them so. Without proper safety procedures, flying is completely useless and definitely *not* a viable means of transportation. If you are planning to pursue a pilot's license, you *must* realize the importance of flight safety. If you feel this statement is the usual drivel that is to be acknowledged and then forgotten, you may find yourself in a most dangerous situation, one which is certainly life-threatening. If you don't plan to concentrate *at least* as much on safety as you do on the other aspects of flying, then do yourself and the aviation world a favor and *forget about flying altogether*.

It has been stated before that flying is inherently safe, but totally unforgiving of mistakes. This is evidenced by the majority of headlines in newspapers which state that most unfortunate flying accidents are eventually attributed to "pilot error." When you receive a private license, this enables you to legally take the role of pilot-in-command of an aircraft. In safe hands, the plane is a benevolent machine which can greatly expand the pursuits of the individual who uses it. When safety is ignored, the plane becomes a deadly weapon, one which can take the life of the pilot, passengers, and people on the ground within seconds. The holder of a private license assumes a great responsibility. Flying is fun, but it is also a very serious undertaking and absolutely must be treated in this manner. By disregarding even *one* safety rule, a pilot-in-command can destroy not only himself but others as well.

Most individuals who are learning to fly and those who have recent private licenses are among some of the safest pilots in the world. It is when the new pilot begins to significantly progress in proficiency that dangerous aspects are often encountered. Simply put, a person in this category may tend to become cocky and over-confident as to his or her abilities to handle the aircraft in *all* types of situations and flying conditions. They are not as cautious as they once were, and here is where a deadly pattern begins to emerge. This is evidenced by flights into marginal weather conditions, landings on questionable fields, and sometimes even by minor aerobatics. We have all heard about the pilot who successfully flew his plane beneath a bridge, under a power line, or into narrow ravines. As flying becomes more routine, some pilots try to come up with unusual ideas to bring back their initial feelings of thrill and excitement. It could be equated with the taking of narcotics, in that the user needs more and more of the drug as time goes on to maintain his high. It might be best to regard the daring pilot as being terribly lucky in managing to fly his plane beneath the bridge instead of playing him up as a modern-day equivalent of Baron Von Richtofen. A pilot should think more about the unfortunate soul who stalled out and killed himself by attempting this same maneuver.

The previous reference to Baron Von Richtofen was really an inappropriate one. Of the many things he was, a daring pilot was not one of them. His successes in shooting down Allied planes in World War I was directly attibutable to his consistency and not his daring. History will verify that he did not attempt unusual maneuvers, as did many of the other pilots on both sides during this era. He was a safe pilot who always attempted to fly in a conventional manner and did so time and again. This consistency paid off for him and he is remembered to this day and held in high regard by most pilots, while his daring peers of the same era have been forgotten.

Consistency pays off in flying. If you consistently follow the rules and regulations and use good common sense, your payment is in the form of relaxation, fun, benefits, and the respect of fellow pilots. If you consistently break these rules, your payment will eventually be a severe accident. Every good pilot puts safety *first* on his checklist and never disregards this vital aspect of aviation.

Regarding an earlier statement, proficiency is most important to flying; but as you improve, don't let this go to your head. When the author sees pilots who seem to feel that they are experienced enough to tackle any situation, he often relates a story told to him by his instructor many years ago.

Man is not physically equipped to fly. To do so requires highly complex machinery. The pilot becomes a part of the machinery and makes it an extension of himself. The most experienced aviators in the world are the birds of the air. They depend upon their ability to fly nearly every day of their lives. And yet, one afternoon in a midwestern town, frozen ducks began to fall from the skies. They were fully feathered and would have appeared nearly normal except for the fact that they were frozen through and through and tended to shatter when striking the earth. This led to explanations of UFOs and all other sorts of celestial phenomena. The fact of the matter is, the ducks died through "pilot error." They had flown too close to a large storm center and were suddenly whisked to extremely high altitudes by one of the updrafts associated with these types of weather conditions. The ducks were completely out of control and could do nothing to prevent their deaths after the updraft took effect. This example of pilot error resulted in almost immediate destruction.

Now, using the story just told as a learning experience, we can safely say that the moral of this story is, "Regardless of how experienced you are, regardless of your natural and instinctive abilities to fly, you had better do it *by the book* or you might end up falling out of the sky."

THE INTERNATIONAL CIVIL AVIATION ORGANIZATION

The ICAO was originally formed in 1944 to implement the decisions taken at the Chicago Convention on Air Transport. The ICAO involves itself in air transport by issuing standardization procedures and equipment. Among the many beneficial things that have come out of this organization are the ICAO Rules of the Air. Since this is an international organization, their basic rules are modified by each country to suit its own particular purposes.

The following is a partial reprint of the International Rules of the Air, many of which apply in the United States. You will notice that many of them are based upon good common sense:

2.3 Responsibility.

2.3.1. Responsibility of pilot-in-command - The pilot-in-command of an aircraft shall, whether manipulating the controls or not, be responsible for the operation of the aircraft in accordance with the rules of the air, except that he may depart from these rules in circumstances that render such departure absolutely necessary in the interests of safety.

2.3.2. Preflight action - Before beginning a flight, the pilot-in-command of an aircraft shall familiarize himself with all available information appropriate to the intended operation. Preflight action for flights away from the vicinity of an aerodrome, and for all IFR flights, shall include a careful study of available current radio reports and forecasts, taking into consideration field requirements and an alternative course of action if the flight cannot be completed as planned.

2.4. Authority. - The pilot in command of an aircraft shall have final authority as to disposition of the aircraft while he is in command.

2.5. Use Of Intoxicating Liquor, Narcotics Or Drugs. - No person shall pilot an aircraft, or act as a flight crew member of an aircraft, while under the influence of intoxicating liquor or any narcotic drug, by reason of which his capacity so to act is impaired.

3.1. Protection Of Persons And Property.

3.1.1. Negligent or reckless operation of an aircraft - An aircraft shall not be operated in a negligent or reckless manner so as to endanger life or property of others.

3.1.2. Minimum safe height - Except when necessary for taking off or landing or except by permission from the appropriate authority, aircraft shall not be flown:

(a) Over the congested areas of cities, towns, or settlements or over an open-air assembly of persons, unless at such a height as will permit, in the event of an emergency arising, a landing to be made without undue hazard to persons or property on the surface; this height shall not be less than 1000 ft. above the highest obstacle within a radius of 2000 ft. from the aircraft;

(b) Elsewhere when as specified in 3.1.2 (a), at a height less than 500 ft. above the ground or water.

3.1.3. Dropping objects - nothing shall be dropped from an aircraft in flight that might create a hazard to persons or property.

3.1.4. Parachute descents - Parachute descents other than emergency descents shall not be made unless authorized by the appropriate authority.

3.1.5. ACROBATIC FLIGHT

3.1.5.1. No aircraft shall be flown acrobatically so as to constitute a hazard to air traffic.

3.1.5.2. Unless authorized by the appropriate authority, no aircraft shall be flown acrobatically over congested areas of cities, towns, or settlements or over an open-air assembly of persons.

3.1.6. Airspace restrictions - Aircraft will not be flown over areas where there are flight restrictions, the particulars of which have been duly published, except in accordance with the conditions of the restriction or by permission of the appropriate authority of the state imposing the restriction.

3.2. Avoidance Of Collisions.

3.2.1. PROXIMITY

3.2.1.1. An aircraft shall not be operated in such proximity to other aircraft as to create a collision hazard.

3.2.1.2. Aircraft shall not be flown in formation except by prearrangement.

3.2.2. Right of Way - The aircraft that has the right of way shall maintain its heading and speed but nothing in these rules shall relieve the pilot in command of an aircraft from the responsibility of taking such action as will best avert collision. An aircraft that is obliged by the following rules to keep out of the way of another shall avoid passing over or under the other, or crossing head of it, unless passing well clear.

3.2.2.1. Approaching head-on - When two aircraft are approaching head-on or approximately so, when there is danger of collision, each shall alter its heading to the right.

3.2.2.2. Converging - When two aircraft are converging at approximately the same altitude, the aircraft that has the other on its right shall give way, except as follows:

(a) Power-driven heavier-than-air aircraft shall give way to airships, gliders, and balloons;

(b) Airships shall give way to gliders and balloons;

(c) Gliders shall give way to balloons;

(d) Power-driven aircraft shall give way to aircraft which are seen to be towing other aircraft or objects.

3.2.2.3. Overtaking - An overtaking aircraft is an aircraft that approaches another from the rear on a line forming an angle of less than 70 degrees with the plane of symmetry of the latter; i.e., is in such a position with reference to the other aircraft that at night it should be unable to see either of the aircraft's navigation lights. An aircraft that is being overtaken has the right of way, and the overtaking aircraft, whether climbing, descending, or in horizontal flight, shall keep out of the way of the other aircraft by altering its heading to the right, and no subsequent change in the relative positions of the two aircraft shall absolve the overtaking aircraft from this obligation until it is entirely passed and clear.

3.2.2.4. LANDING

3.2.2.4.1. An aircraft in flight, or operating on the ground or water, shall give way to other aircraft landing or on final approach to land.

3.2.2.4.2. When two or more heavier-than-air aircraft are approaching an aerodrome for the purpose of landing, aircraft at the higher altitude shall give way to aircraft at the lower altitude, but the latter shall not take advantage of this rule to cut in front of another which is on final approach to land, or to overtake that aircraft. Nevertheless, power-driven, heavier-than-air aircraft shall give way to gliders.

3.2.2.4.3. Emergency landing - An aircraft that is aware that another is compelled to land shall give way to that aircraft.

3.2.2.5. Taking off - An aircraft about to take off shall not attempt to do so until there is no apparent risk of collision with another aircraft.

3.2.3. Towing objects - No object shall be towed by an aircraft, except in accordance with requirements prescribed by the appropriate authority.

3.2.4. Lights to be displayed by aircraft - Between sunset and sunrise, or such other period between sunset and sunrise as may be prescribed by the appropriate authority, all aircraft in flight or operating on the maneuvering area of an aerodrome shall display lights ads defined by the appropriate authority.

3.2.5. Simulated instrument flights - An aircraft shall not be flown under simulated instrument flight conditions unless:

(a) Fully functioning dual controls are installed in the aircraft; and

(b) A competent pilot occupies a control seat to act as safety pilot for the person who is flying under simulated instrument conditions. The safety pilot shall have adequate vision forward and to each side of the aircraft, or a competent observer in communication with the safety pilot shall occupy a position in the aircraft from which his field of vision adequately supplements that of the safety pilot.

3.2.6. OPERATION ON, AND IN THE VICINITY OF AN AERODROME

3.2.6.1. An aircraft operated on, or in the vicinity of an aerodrome shall:

(a) Observe other aerodrome traffic for the purpose of avoiding collisions;

(b) Conform with or avoid the pattern of traffic by other aircraft in operation;

(c) Make all turns to the left, when approaching for a landing and after taking off, unless otherwise instructed;

(d) Land and take off into the wind unless safety or air traffic considerations determine that a different direction is preferable.

3.2.7. WATER OPERATIONS

3.2.7.1. When two aircraft, or an aircraft and a vessel, are approaching one another and there is a risk of collision, the aircraft shall proceed with careful regard to existing circumstances and conditions, including the limitations of the respective craft.

3.2.7.1.1. Converging - An aircraft which has another aircraft or vessel on its right shall give way so as to keep well clear.

3.2.7.1.2. Approaching head-on - An aircraft approaching another aircraft or vessel head on, or approximately so, shall alter its heading to the right to keep well clear.

3.2.7.1.3. Overtaking - The aircraft or vessel which is being overtaken has the right of way, and the one overtaking shall alter its heading to keep well clear.

3.2.7.1.4. Landing and takeoff - Aircraft landing on, or taking off from the water shall, insofar as practicable, keep well clear of all vessels and avoid impeding their navigation.

3.2.7.2. Lights to be displayed by aircraft on the water - Between sunset and sunrise, or other such period between sunset and sunrise as may be prescribed by the appropriate authority, all aircraft on the water shall display lights as defined by the authority, unless within an especially exempted area. No other lights shall be displayed by such aircraft if they are likely to be mistaken for these lights.

3.2.7.3. In areas in which the International Regulations for Preventing Collisions at Sea are in force, aircraft on the water shall, in addition to those covered by 3.2.7.1. and 3.2.7.2., comply with such other of the regulations as are pertinent.

THE FATAL ACCIDENT PILOT

The Federal Aviation Administration has often voiced the opinion that the automobile ride to the airport is statistically the most dangerous aspect of flying. The National Transportation Safety Board has figures which show that more people die on a yearly basis from boating, driving, and even walking down the street than from accidents involving light aircraft. The FAA has developed a profile based on all aircraft accidents, which says a few things about the pilot who is most likely to have a fatal accident.

He (or she) is usually between the ages of 30 and 50 and earns an income which allows him to pilot a late model aircraft. The aircraft may be owned outright, leased, or rented. He has more than 50, but less than 100 hours of flight time. (Notice that this completely precludes the student pilot who needs a minimum of 40 hours to attain a private license.) The FAA goes on to say that this pilot will be non-instrument rated and will be flying in marginal weather conditions. He will almost always fail to get a weather briefing and he will not file a flight plan. He will most often be flying in conditions of low ceilings and low visibility. The accident is most likely to happen on a weekend trip, taking in the days of Friday, Saturday, or Sunday. Vacation time in the summer and special holidays in November, December, and January are the most likely periods for the accident to occur.

The FAA continues by stating that *this pilot's first accident will be his last. He will be most often killed by the impact.* The criteria presented here indicates that an accident is most likely to occur to a person who has recently received a private pilot's license and has flown for a considerable number of hours thereafter. This is where over-confidence sets in. To repeat an oft-used phrase in this book, *"Flying is very unforgiving of mistakes."*

WEATHER CONDITIONS

Time and again, weather is listed as a cause of aviation accidents. This is usually not exactly accurate. It would be more proper to say that weather was a factor, but the true cause was the pilot who flew into unknown weather or conditions which he or she was unable to handle. In marginal conditions, the VFR pilot may be flying legally; but in a very short period of time, marginal VFR conditions can quickly change to full IFR. As was noted in the FAA report, most pilots do not get a weather briefing before flying off to their awaiting fates. This is the breaking of a cardinal rule of aviation which states that the pilot will find out *everything he can* about present and future weather conditions which have any possibility at all of becoming a factor during an intended flight.

Today, there is *no excuse* for a pilot to omit obtaining the proper weather information. With modern weather forecasting systems, observation networks, and compiled reports, the weather along almost any flight path should present few surprises to the person who has bothered to check with his FSS (Flight Service Station). This is done by making a quick phone call.

Student pilots are taught from the beginning to stay away from thunderstorms and icing conditions. The multitude of wind currents found within and around a storm front are often of magnitudes which can quickly cause structural failure to light, as well as heavy aircraft. Commercial jets do not fly through thunderstorms; they fly over them. If they can't do this, then they go around.

There are two forms of icing conditions. One involves the forming of ice on the surface of the airplane, while the other affects the engine carburetor, choking all airflow. Structural icing develops when an aircraft flies into conditions of visible moisture and when the temperature is around 32 degrees or less. Neophyte pilots assume that this condition is most prevalent in the cold winter months, but it is a fact that it can occur on hot summer days when the aircraft is at high altitudes where the temperature is far less than that found at ground level.

When ice forms on the wings, fuselage and propeller of an aircraft, the overall weight of the plane is affected, as is its aerodynamic drag. Simply put, the plane is far heavier than usual and its structure has been altered so that it does not pass through the air so easily. This means the plane will stall out at higher than normal air speeds.

The other form of icing affects the air intake and the carburetor. When air intakes are affected, similar conditions to those which cause structural icing are usually present. Carburetor icing fools a lot of new pilots. It seldom occurs when air temperatures are very low, because much of the time there is little moisture present. This type of icing occurs during conditions of moderate temperatures when the relative humidity is very high. When air is drawn into the engine through its induction system, its pressure is reduced in the carburetor. This, combined with the vaporized fuel, can cause the air temperature to drop by 40 degrees or more. 68 Degrees Fahrenheit is the temperature reading which is most often stressed as being very dangerous to beginning pilots. Subtract roughly 40 degrees for the cooling effects at the carburetor and you're faced with an actual temperature in this area of the powerplant of about 28 degrees. We're talking about very moist air in this example with a humidity factor approaching 100%. Given all of these factors, the moisture content will quickly be transformed into ice which chokes off the air supply and kills the engine. Due to this danger, carbureted aircraft are equipped with heaters which are manually activated and heat the incoming air to prevent ice from forming. The heat is taken from the engine manifold.

The carburetor heat control on a light aircraft is designed to *prevent* icing. It is *not* meant to melt ice which has already formed. Once your engine has been deprived of its air supply and has ceased to function, activating the carburetor heat control may have little effect.

From a safety standpoint, pilots are cautioned to avoid flying into known structural icing conditions. Regarding induction icing, a check of the carburetor heating device is standard procedure before taking off. The heater is normally activated before backing off on the throttle, as this is where the maximum danger lies. During certain conditions, the plane may be flown with a partial amount of carburetor heat, but normally this device is only activated when power is substantially reduced because the engine produces less horsepower when carburetor heat is being applied.

OTHER SAFETY PRECAUTIONS

The term "pilot-in-command" should be taken quite literally. This means that as the pilot of an aircraft, you must be in total command of yourself, your craft, and all conditions which affect safe flying. If there are other people in the plane with you, you must exercise complete control over them in addition to your other responsibilities. Small children can easily interfere with a pilot's ability to safely fly his aircraft should they become restless or begin to engage in horseplay. Children, as well as all other passengers, should be instructed before the flight as to their proper behavior. Children adapt readily to changing situation and environments and are more apt to cause problems than the adults you carry. The latter do not adapt as easily and may be somewhat apprehensive about flying if they haven't had a lot of experience in this area. You are responsible for your plane and for your passengers, so beware of those who are under the influence of alcohol, ill, or extremely upset. If the carrying of these passengers represents even a slight hazard to flight safety, then you are not only foolish for allowing them in your aircraft, but in violation of FAA regulations as well.

From a purely common sense standpoint, it should be apparent that you should not act as pilot-in-command of an aircraft when you are upset and not in the proper frame of mind to handle an emergency situation should one develop. FAA rules are very specific regarding the flying of an aircraft when you have alcohol in your system. This is against the law and can quickly earn you a license revocation and a fine—if you are fortunate enough to be alive after the flight. Flying is relaxing for most pilots, but don't use this privilege as a means of getting rid of tension when you are highly upset or frustrated. Safe pilots have clear, alert minds. But they are human and cannot always maintain this mental balance. We all have our problems from time to time, so even the most proficient pilot, the one with the perfect safety record, is not capable of being an adequate pilot 100% of the time . . . but he or she had better be during 100% of the time when serving as pilot-in-command of an aircraft. This can all be boiled down to a very simple rule: *Don't fly when you're not 100% on the ball.* If you do, you may be 100% dead. A condition which might only be a slight mental or physical handicap on the ground will be greatly amplified at higher altitudes. If you're not perfect when you take off, you're going to be in a far worse state when you begin to climb.

SUMMARY

Many, many entire books have been written on the subject of pilot safety. It is an instrumental and continuous exercise which is taught from Day One of your training program. It will be an integral part of your flying pursuits for the rest of your life. Admittedly, this chapter has strayed quite a bit from the book's original intent, which was to demonstrate the pleasurable aspects of flying. What was talked about here was not exactly pleasurable but is absolutely *necessary* in order to pursue the more pleasing aspects discussed elsewhere. In most aircraft accidents, only the pilot is to blame. This is not to say that only perfect people should fly airplanes. There are no such animals, but if you perfectly adhere to the rules of safety stressed throughout your aviation training, you will be doing everything that is in your power to maintain a very adequate safety margin. This will enable you to truly enjoy all that flying has to offer, year after year after year.

Glossary

ADF: An abbreviation for *Automatic Direction Finder*, which is an electronic instrument that utilizes the transmissions of ground base medium frequency radio stations of known location in determining the flight course of an aircraft in relation to these stations.

ARTCC: An abbreviation for *air route traffic control center*, of which there are 28 in the United States. These centers jointly coordinate IFR traffic between their assigned areas.

ATIS: An abbreviation for *Automatic Terminal Information Service*, which provides recorded information at major air terminals. This data gives arriving and departing pilots advance information on weather conditions, communication frequencies, and runways at various facilities.

absolute altitude: The altitude of an airplane above the surface of the terrain over which it is flying.

absolute ceiling: A term used to rate aircraft performance, which means the absolute altitude above sea level at which the craft may be operated.

active runway: A runway in use at a particular time at an airport facility. This is normally the runway which has the most favorable wind conditions.

ailerons: Hinged surfaces lying on the outer trailing wing section of an aircraft which are controlled by the stick or yoke in the cockpit and determine rate of turn.

Air Traffic Control: Abbreviated ATC, an extensive network of communications facilities which are divided into terminal and in-route services and are designed to provide weather information, traffic separation and general help to pilots in command.

aircraft oxygen system: Normally used in unpressurized aircraft when flying at altitudes approaching and exceeding 10,000 feet, this system includes an oxygen bottle, hoses, and masks to assure pilots and passengers an adequate oxygen supply.

airfoil: Any physical shape which is designed to produce life when air is passed over its surface.

AIRMET: An in-flight advisory to pilots warning of potentially hazardous meteorological conditions which may present a danger to limited capability aircraft.

airport advisory: An in-flight bulletin to pilots providing information on conditions at a specific airport facility.

airport directory: A directory of all airports, seaplane bases, and heliports which can be used by general aviation aircraft within the United States.

airport lighting: A lighting system which encompasses runway lights and any other illuminating indications of an airport facility.

airport traffic area: A physical zone extending outward in all directions from an airport facility for a specific distance which also includes the airspace above this area to a specific altitude.

airport traffic pattern: A standardized routing of incoming and outgoing aircraft at an aircraft facility. For example, a landing pattern might include a downwind leg, base leg, and final leg.

airspace, controlled: An airport traffic area in which all aircraft must receive instructions as to course and altitude from a control tower.

airspace, uncontrolled: Any airspace within which the FAA Air Traffic Control does not have responsibility to exercise specific control over an aircraft.

alternator: A transducer which generates electricity directly from the rotation of an aircraft engine.

altimeter: An aircraft instrument which acts upon changes in atmospheric pressure and indicates altitude above sea level.

altitude: In general terms, the distance of an airplane above sea level. See absolute altitude.

ammeter: An electrical device which indicates the flow of current in an aircraft electrical system.

angle of attack: The angle at which the leading edge of an airfoil intercepts the air.

approach control: An airport control facility which gives specific instructions to pilots preparing to land.

approach lights: Lights which are placed immediately in front of an airport runway which indicate the runway center line to approaching pilots.

approach speed: The recommended speed at which a specific aircraft is to be flown when preparing for a landing. This figure is usually supplied by the manufacturer and is given for various flap settings.

area forecasts: A weather forecast provided by the National Weather Service Office which is distributed by teletype to airports and various commercial broadcasting facilities.

asymetrical thrust: Uneven thrust valve which is most often applied to the propeller of an airplane. Due to the different angles of attack, greater thrust is produced from one side of the propeller than from the other.

attitude gyro: Also called the artificial horizon, an instrument which portrays in picture form the actual attitude of an airplane with respect to level ground.

aviation weather report: An hourly report by a weather station which constantly updates itself based upon current weather conditions as reported to them by pilots.

azimuth: In celestial navigation, the true bearing of any heavenly body.

barometer: A device used to measure atmospheric pressure or weight of the atmosphere.

base leg: The 90 degree turn from the downwind leg of a landing approach. While on this leg, an aircraft will begin its descent from the downwind altitude.

best angle-of-climb: An aircraft performance rating given by the manufacturer which will bring about an airspeed designed to attain the greatest gain in altitude over a given distance.

best rate-of-climb: An aircraft performance rating given by the manufacturer which will bring about an airspeed designed to attain the greatest gain in altitude over a specific time period.

cabin: The interior of the aircraft fuselage in which passengers and/or baggage are transported.

camber: The curvature of the upper and lower surfaces of an airfoil.

carburetor heat: A heating system attached to the carburetor of an aircraft powerplant which ducts outside air through a heating element and allows the hot air to pass through the carburetor in order to prevent the formation of ice.

ceiling: The height above the ground to the lowest layer of cloud aloft.

center of gravity: A point in an aircraft around which it can be perfectly balanced.

chart: A map of the earth's surface designed especially for aviation uses and which indicates ground features that may easily be identified by pilots.

checkpoint: A physical object or landmark which can be easily identified from the air and which serves as a course reference for a pilot.

chord line: An imaginary straight line drawn from the leading edge to the trailing edge of an airfoil.

climb performance: The specified ability of an aircraft to gain altitude under set conditions of temperature, weather, and height above sea level.

closed runway: A runway at an airport facility that is closed to all operations. This is often indicated by large "X" marks painted on the runway and visible from the air.

cockpit: A general term describing the portion of an aircraft cabin where the pilot or pilots control the aircraft.

communication system: Generally speaking, a radio station located within an aircraft designed to transmit and receive information.

compass, magnetic: A direction seeking instrument used in aircraft to indicate course headings.

computer, flight: A multi-function, mechanical calculator used by pilots to determine time, speed, and distance readings when plotting a course.

constant-speed propeller: A propeller with the ability to rotate its individual blades in order to seek the best angle of attack for a given rpm speed.

control tower: The main communication site at a controlled airport. This system is normally located in a high tower from which control operators have a panoramic view of the entire facility. Control tower operators are responsible for control of all airplane traffic within the control area.

controlled airspace: See *airspace, controlled.*

crosswind: A steady air current which impacts the aircraft from its left or right side as opposed to a tailwind or a headwind, blowing from behind and ahead, respectively.

cylinder head temperature: An indication of engine cooling efficiency taken by measurement of the temperature of one of the aft cylinder heads.

DME: Abbreviation for *distance measuring equipment,* a system whereby an airborne transmitter sends a signal to a ground station which receives this communication and answers with a coded signal. The airborne equipment measures the time interval between the transmission and the reply and converts this information into a direct readout of distance between the aircraft and the ground station.

density altitude: Pressure altitude readings which have been corrected for non-standard temperature.

directional gyro: A heading indicator which is designed to function without the error factor which is inherent in all magnetic compasses. It has no direction seeking properties and is set to headings shown by a magnetic compass.

directional stability: A description of an aircraft's tendency to fly in a straight direction. This assumes completely stable wind conditions and is a rating of the plane's structural design.

downwind leg: In an airport traffic pattern, the leg which the plane flies that is parallel with the runway but in the opposite direction of the intended landing.

drift: The amount of deviation from a flow course heading that is caused by crosswind conditions.

dual ignition system: A standard aircraft electrical system which duplicates each component as a safety factor. A typical dual ignition system will contain two magnetos and each cylinder head will be fitted with two spark plugs.

electrical system: In an aircraft, the electrical components which include the battery, alternator, regulator and all other devices which are a part of or operate from an electrical power source.

elevators: Control surfaces located at the aft end of the airplane which are controlled by the wheel or stick. Depending on attitude, the elevator will cause the tail of the plane to rise or fall.

empennage: The rear portion of an airplane consisting of a vertical stabilizer, rudder, horizontal stabilizer, and elevator.

FAA: Abbreviation for *Federal Aviation Administration*, the Federal agency which regulates the use of aircraft.

FSS: Abbreviation for *Flight Service Station*, a major communications facility which pilots use to receive in-flight advisory information.

field elevation: The altitude of an airport above sea level.

final approach: The last leg of a landing pattern which is formed by making a 90 degree turn from the base leg. The final approach aligns the aircraft with the runway as the pilot prepares to touch down.

fixed pitch propeller: As opposed to a constant speed propeller, a propeller having a blade angle which cannot be changed by the pilot.

flaps: Surfaces installed on the inboard trailing edge portions of aircraft wing sections which are used to change the camber of the airfoil. Flaps are used during takeoff and landing and in other flight maneuvers to effect the lift-to-drag ratio of their craft.

flight control system: Generally, the moveable surfaces of an aircraft which includes the ailerons, elevators, rudder, stabilators, and trim system.

fuel system: Those components in an aircraft which deal specifically with the delivering of fuel and air to the powerplant. These include the carburetor, fuel pump, mixture control, tanks, air intake, and many other components.

fuselage: The body of the airplane that provides a central attachment point for the wing, empennage, landing gear, and powerplant.

glider: An aircraft with excellent aerodynamic characteristics which has no powerplant and is towed to altitude where it is released and remains aloft by taking full advantage of ascending air currents.

gross weight: The maximum weight at which an aircraft is designed to operate.

ground control: At a controlled airport, the persons and systems that provide control of aircraft which have landed or are about to taxi to a runway for departure.

ground effect: An area between the earth and a flying aircraft equivalent to roughly the distance of the aircraft wing span where induced drag is significantly reduced. When an aircraft flies within this area, it is said to be flying in *ground effect.*

ground speed— The speed of an aircraft in relationship to the ground. A ground speed of 100 mph means the aircraft, within one hour's time, will cover 100 miles of ground space when flying in a straight line.

gyroplane: A type of rotorcraft which attains thrust with a pusher-type propeller. Lift is provided by means of a free-wheeling rotor, as opposed to a driven rotor in a true helicopter.

heading: The direction an aircraft takes in flight.

helicopter: A rotorcraft on which a powered rotor is engaged in order to achieve lift.

hypoxia: A partial lack of oxygen, as opposed anoxia, which is a complete lack of oxygen. The threat of hypoxia is a constant hazard in high altitude flying.

ICAO: An abbreviation for *International Civil Aviation Organization* which was formed in 1944 to bring about a degree of standardization for procedures and equipment dealing with aircraft and flying.

icing conditions: Generally, a description of a weather condition, often at a specific altitude, which will tend to create ice which can build up on the structure of an aircraft.

IFR: An abbreviation for Instrument Flight Rules, often used as a description for weather conditions which require navigation instruments. An IFR pilot is one who has been licensed as qualified to fly on instruments in IFR weather conditions.

ignition system: See *dual ignition system.*

indicated airspeed: The direct instrument reading a pilot obtains from the airspeed indicator which gives a readout of the speed of the air passing across the aircraft wing.

in-flight advisory: A service to pilots by the National Weather Service which is disseminated by a FSS by radio and warning of possible hazardous weather conditions which may be significantly worse than originally forecast.

inversion, temperature: An atmospheric condition where temperature increases with an increase in altitude instead of decreasing as it normally will do.

landing distance: A specification on the capabilities of an aircraft normally supplied by the manufacturer stating the average distance or runway length required to land the plane and come to a full stop in average conditions.

landing gear: Generally, the undercarriage of an aircraft consisting of three wheels and associated struts. Some plans may utilize a nosewheel, while others may use a conventional gear configuration with a tailwheel. Landing gear may also include floats for amphibious operations, or even skis for landing on snow and ice.

landing performance: A rating given an aircraft to describe its general tendencies during a landing. This rating begins at touchdown and continues on the rollout to a full stop. It may also include the general slow speed handling of the aircraft immediately before touchdown.

lateral axis: The revolution of an aircraft about its center of gravity point which is controlled by the elevators. When an airplane climbs or dives, movement is produced around the lateral axis.

lateral stability: A measurement of an aircraft's stability to hold the wing tips in position during level flight, assuming there is no outside force to interfere with them.

longitudinal axis: Also called the *roll axis*, the rotation of an airplane which is controlled by the ailerons and causes one wing section to dip while the other one rises.

longitudinal stability: The ability of an aircraft to keep its nose in level flight, assuming no outside interference is present. When an aircraft is *longitudinally stable*, it will return to level flight when outside forces have caused it to deviate from this configuration.

magneto: The basic source of current in an aircraft ignition system, a magneto consists of a permanent magnet connected to a shaft which is rotated by the crankshaft of the engine. The magneto can generate a voltage output of 20,000 volts, which is used to jump a spark plug gap and ignite the fuel.

manifold pressure gauge: An instrument used in aircraft with constant speed propellers in order to determine proper throttle setting. Its readout is calibrated in inches of mercury.

markings: Generally speaking, painted indications on airport runways or immediately preceding them which provide landing information to pilots.

NOTAMs: An abbreviation for *Notices to Airmen*, these are included at the close of some aviation weather reports to indicate information of interest to pilots regarding an airport.

oil pressure gauge: One of the primary engine instruments which indicates the pressure in pounds per square inch under which the oil of the engine lubricating system is being supplied.

oil temperature gauge: Another basic powerplant instrument which is normally used in conjunction with the oil pressure gauge and which gives a readout in degrees Fahrenheit.

oleo strut: A shock-absorbing strut to which the wheels of most airplanes are attached. An oleo strut is a hydraulic device which provides controlled compression upon touchdown.

PIREPs: An abbreviation for *Pilot Reports*, the weather information which is reported by pilots in flight and which is disseminated by the FSS.

pitch: The up and down movement of the nose of an aircraft. Pitch is controlled by the elevators.

pitot tube: A major component in the static or pressure system of an aircraft used to drive certain flight instruments. Impact pressure with the air is taken from the pitot tube and fed through pressure lines to these instruments.

powerplant: The aircraft engine.

propeller: An airfoil driven by the powerplant which converts engine shaft torque into thrust.

restricted area: An area of airspace in which the flight of an aircraft is subject to certain limitations which may include altitude, speed, and heading.

rotorcraft: An aircraft which uses an overhead rotor which may or may not receive direct power from the engine. The *helicopter* uses a powered rotor in order to achieve life, while a *gyroplane* has a free-wheeling rotor and a pusher propeller.

rudder: A hinged assembly on the empennage of an aircraft which is used to turn the tail left and right.

rudder pedals: Foot controls in the cockpit of an aircraft which are linked to the rudder. Pushing the left pedal causes the rudder to force the tail to the right. The right pedal does the opposite.

service ceiling: An altitude rating given specific airplanes by manufacturers which indicates the maximum altitude which a craft may be operated at while maintaining generally normal flight and operational characteristics.

stabilizer: The horizontal section of the empennage to which the elevators are attached.

STOL: An abbreviation for *short take-off and landing* and used to describe an aircraft with the design characteristics which allows unusually short runway facilities.

stall: A condition where an aircraft's wings lose lift and it starts to fall. This can be produced by too little airspeed or too high an angle of attack.

tachometer: A major powerplant instrument which reads engine rpms.

takeoff distance: A manufacturer's rating given to a specific aircraft indicating the normal distance or runway required for liftoff at sea level.

takeoff performance: The general handling characteristics of an aircraft upon takeoff which may include its climbout speed and stability.

tetrahedron: A streamlined wind indicator which is designed so that its pointed end will always turn into the wind. This device is visible from the air to provide pilots with a visual indication of wind direction.

threshold lighting: Green lights which are placed on the front or threshold of a runway to indicate to pilots the beginning of the usable runway.

trim tabs: A small hinged section on the aircraft elevator used to relieve certain control pressures and prevent pilot fatigue. The trim tabs are used to finely set the elevator so the plane will maintain level flight on its own without the pilot having to apply undue force on the yoke.

true airspeed: The actual speed of the aircraft through the air mass.

true course: The intended or actual path over the ground of an aircraft in flight.

turbulence: Air current conditions which tend to cause an aircraft to deviate from its course heading or which interfere with smooth flight characteristics.

usable fuel: Generally, a manufacturer's rating which may differ from aircraft to aircraft and states the amount of fuel held in the tanks which can be actually fed to the powerplant. A small quantity of fuel in the tanks remains below the positive feed points and cannot be depended upon. Also a rating given by manufacturers to describe the amount of fuel which can be carried by an aircraft when transporting a specific number of passengers or amount of cargo.

VFR: An abbreviation for *Visual Flight Rules* and a description of weather conditions which allow the pilot to fly an aircraft along a course which will provide visible ground checkpoints.

VOR: An abbreviation for very high frequency omni-directional range, a radio system made up of transmitting ground stations whose signals are received at the aircraft and used for navigation purposes.

VTOL: An abbreviation for vertical take-off and landing and which is applied to helicopters and other such devices which can lift off vertically from a dead stop and require no runways as such.

wind sock: The most common wind indicating device at an airport facility consisting of a flexible cone through which the wind blows, causing the small end to stand out and point away from the wind.

wing: The major airfoil of an airplane containing the flaps and ailerons.

Index

Index